Wallace and Bates
in the
Tropics

Wallace and Bates in the Tropics

— • —

AN INTRODUCTION TO THE THEORY OF NATURAL SELECTION

edited by

Barbara G. Beddall

Based on the writings of Alfred Russel Wallace
and Henry Walter Bates

THE MACMILLAN COMPANY
Collier-Macmillan Ltd., London

The Macmillan Company
Collier-Macmillan Canada, Ltd., Toronto, Ontario

Library of Congress catalog card number: 69-12174
Maps by Rafael D. Palacios
Printed in the United States of America
First Printing

To Ned and Tommy

Introduction

An understanding of biological principles is essential to safeguarding the future of our world. One of the most important of these is the theory of evolution by means of natural selection. Two contemporaries of Charles Darwin, Alfred Russel Wallace and Henry Walter Bates, played major although less well-known roles in the nineteenth century drama of its discovery. It is the editor's hope that the following selections taken from the writings of these two men will provide a readable introduction to these fundamental ideas.

Self-taught naturalists both, Wallace and Bates between them spent a total of twenty-three years exploring the tropics. To support themselves they traveled as commercial collectors, but even before leaving England in 1848 they were fascinated by the unanswered question, what was the origin of species?

Wallace finally worked out the theory of natural selection in 1858 and sent an outline of it to Darwin from the Malay Archipelago, precipitating the publication of the *Origin of Species* in 1859. Bates worked out his theory of mimicry, "a most beautiful proof" of the theory of natural selection, after his return home. And, in the tradition of the times, they both published marvelous accounts of their travels and discoveries: Wallace wrote *A Narrative of Travels on the Amazon and Rio Negro* (1853) and *The Malay Archipelago* (1869), and Bates wrote *The Naturalist on the River Amazons* (1863). The majority of the selections are taken from these three books, with some additional material from other pertinent sources. Exact references to all the quoted material are given in the Notes and Sources.

The selections have been chosen primarily to give an idea of the diversity of the tropics, the many different forms of life to be found there, their interrelationships, and their geographical distribution. It was from this complexity that Wallace and Bates distilled some general principles applicable to life everywhere. Besides this, both men had a sense of adventure and an eye for beauty, as other selections show. In the section on South America, the selections from Wallace and Bates have been interspersed, the writer being indicated each time there is a change from one to the other. The chronology and the maps (drawn by Rafael D. Palacios) will help the reader to locate each of the travelers.

Geographical and other names have in most

cases been modernized to conform to present usage, with the exception of the scientific names of butterflies, and paragraphing and punctuation have been modernized. This seemed desirable for consistency because Wallace and Bates did not always agree with each other in matters of style, spelling, or names. At the same time it is hoped that these changes will prove useful to the modern reader. Earlier names or variations in spelling will be found in the Index.

Meanings of foreign or otherwise obscure words have been added to the text in brackets, and definitions of important terms will be found in the Glossary.

For those seeking additional information, some useful magazine articles are listed in **For Further Reading.**

Finally, the editor wishes to offer a word of appreciation for the use of the invaluable collections of the Bridgeport (Connecticut) Public Library and the New York Public Library, and of thanks to Miklos Pinther of the American Geographical Society and to Grace Davall of the New York Zoological Society for help with some of the difficult names.

—Barbara G. Beddall
Fairfield, Connecticut, 1968

Contents

Maps will be found on pages 27 and 145

prologue

It should be remembered too that the want
in those days of modern facilities which are
only fair and right, prevented all but the
most determined or the fortunate from following science. Scientific men were, therefore, comparatively few. . . .

THE ROYAL SOCIETY

"THE MOST
DETERMINED"

I should like to take some one family to
study thoroughly, principally with a view
to the origin of species. By that means I am
strongly of opinion that some definite re-
sults might be arrived at.

WALLACE TO BATES, EARLY 1848

■ "The most determined or the fortunate"—these
words aptly describe the indefatigable men who were
to follow scientific careers in the England of a century ago. The more fortunate had university educa-
tions and sometimes private incomes as well, but a
few remarkable men had neither. All were determined. These scientists may have been "comparatively few" in numbers, but they were the giants of
an era that revolutionized man's approach to the natural world about him.

Who were these men? Where did they come
from? What did they accomplish?

The most outstanding name of this period belongs, of course, to Charles Darwin. To him goes the

credit for establishing a method, natural selection, by which the evolution of plants and animals could have occurred.

The theory of evolution was the concept that came to dominate nineteenth century thought. It belongs particularly to the field of biology, but its influence spilled over into other fields as well. It was not a new idea when Darwin published his book *On the Origin of Species* in 1859. Even natural selection as a mechanism of change had been proposed many years earlier, although it had passed unnoticed. It was Darwin, however, who put these two ideas together and backed them up with evidence painstakingly accumulated over many years to show how evolution could have occurred.

What are species, and why should there be a question about their origin?

Today a species can be briefly defined as a population of interbreeding individuals. We easily recognize robins as one species of bird, for instance, and crows as another. It is also believed that these species are descended from predecessor species and that they have evolved over a long period of time through the gradual accumulation of inherited variations.

Before the Darwinian revolution, however, a species was thought to have been "created" in a permanently unchanging form. In fact a literal reading of the Bible had led men to believe in the recent creation of the earth and all its inhabitants, and an actual date, 4004 B.C., had been worked out by James Usher, Archbishop of Armagh. If this were so, there would of course be no question about the origin, or the beginning, of species, for they would all have been created in 4004 B.C.

It was recognized that species varied, that there

were differences between individuals, but these varieties were not understood. In general they were looked upon as nuisances that interfered with an easy and clear-cut definition of a species.

And the whole, the earth and all its inhabitants, was thought to have been created especially for man's benefit and use (at least in Western civilization). This led man to inflate his own importance and, in consequence, to misunderstand and misuse the natural world around him. Such attitudes have muddled his efforts to unravel nature's mysteries even to the present day.

Geology is the study of the physical properties of the earth—of the rocks, the mountains, the rivers—and of the forces that have shaped them. One of the early puzzles that turned up was how to interpret fossils, the animal- and plant-like traces found in the rocks. Some thought they were merely accidental resemblances to living forms, others that they had been made by evil forces to confuse men's minds. Still others, known as catastrophists, believed that fossils were actually records of earlier creatures (as indeed they are) that had been wiped out by cataclysms such as the flood.

An important step toward the theory of evolution was the growing realization that the earth's history was far longer than the six thousand years allotted by Usher. Another was that this history was not a haphazard set of circumstances defying investigation. Rather, the earth itself provides a long record of events that can be studied, and fossils, which give evidence of this past, have become valuable clues to what has happened to the earth and to its inhabitants.

And so a question that hardly existed before acquired a nagging insistence. What was the origin of species? Where had all the species that had existed at different times come from?

The question was not easy to answer. It required a fresh look at the natural world and a linking together of ideas from various fields of knowledge. Besides this, the formation of a new species is itself very difficult to observe. It is not a sudden, spectacular event like the lighting of a fire. It is a slow and gradual change that takes place over a long period of time.

There was another stumbling block. The impact of the theory of evolution lies in its challenge to established thinking about man's place in the scheme of things. It showed that man was a part of the whole, not a superior being for whom it had all been created. Naturally such a change in emphasis was fiercely resisted. But if one takes time to think about it, what has actually happened is no less remarkable than a sudden creation, and man is, as far as we know at present, the most intelligent being that has so far evolved.

Darwin's is the best-known name, but there are others who also contributed to this revolution; their names shine less brightly only because of the unusual brilliance of Darwin's. Among them are the geologist Sir Charles Lyell, the biologist Thomas Huxley, the botanist Sir Joseph Hooker, the publisher and author Robert Chambers, and finally, the two friends and fellow naturalists, Alfred Russel Wallace and Henry Walter Bates.

In a sense all the naturalists of this period, even Darwin, were self-taught amateurs. Professional education at that time led to careers only in medicine, law, or the church. Furthermore, religious tests were required for university matriculation and for fellowships, and they imposed a rigid interpretation of the natural world and of man's place in it. Darwin first studied medicine, following in his father's footsteps, but then changed to the ministry; Hooker and Huxley both had medical degrees, and Lyell was admitted to the bar.

Darwin's interest in natural history began with insects, and he became an avid beetle collector. He also acquired some knowledge of geology and botany during his years at Cambridge University. Hooker's father was a prominent botanist (also largely self-taught), and the son was exposed to the study of plants from earliest childhood. Lyell, whose father was a botanist of sorts, had started by collecting insects and then at Oxford had turned to the study of geology. Darwin and Lyell came from wealthy families and could indulge their hobbies without any financial worries, but Hooker and Huxley were always pressed for money.

Chambers, Wallace, and Bates did not have the same opportunities, coming as they did from less educated and less affluent families. All three left school at the early age of thirteen or fourteen in order to earn their livings. Chambers became a successful publisher. He was also the anonymous author of an early, widely read book on evolution, *Vestiges of the Natural History of Creation.*

Wallace and Bates may have lacked the advantages of a university education, but they shared another kind of education with Darwin, Hooker, and Huxley, and that was travel. All these inquisitive and observant men made lengthy journeys to far corners of the world, eagerly collecting specimens of the nat-

Alfred Russel Wallace

ural history of these places and absorbing impressions. And they also had time to reflect and think, one of the advantages of the slower methods of travel of those days over the jets of today.

Darwin spent five years exploring the continent of South America as an unpaid naturalist on the staff of the surveying ship H.M.S. *Beagle,* a post for which he had been recommended by his botany professor at Cambridge. Although he had hitherto been an indifferent scholar, he was keenly interested in natural history and kept careful notes of all that he saw. On his return home he wrote a vivid account of his travels and observations, the still justly famous *Voyage of the Beagle.*

Henry Walter Bates
(COURTESY OF THE ROYAL
GEOGRAPHICAL SOCIETY)

Hooker and Huxley also traveled extensively, Hooker as assistant surgeon and botanist to Sir James Ross's expedition to the Antarctic and Huxley as surgeon aboard H.M.S. *Rattlesnake* on its surveying mission to Torres Strait, between New Guinea and Australia. Both men were able to combine their medical assignments with the study of natural history. Like Darwin, they made numerous collections and observations on plants and animals, educating themselves as they went along. A few years later Hooker made another trip, this time to Sikkim in the Himalaya Mountains, where he collected plants for the Royal Botanic Gardens at Kew.

There were few paid jobs for naturalists as such,

and so Wallace and Bates, penniless but enthusiastic amateurs, took a different tack. They became commercial collectors and supported their travels by collecting specimens of animals and selling them to museums or private collectors. Bates spent eleven years in the Amazon Basin of Brazil; Wallace spent four years in the same area and then another eight on the opposite side of the world in the Malay Archipelago. Not only did they make valuable contributions to science, but each also wrote excellent books on his travels which rival Darwin's for readability, adventure, and scientific interest.

Although their roles in the evolutionary drama may be less well known, Wallace and Bates each became important in his own right. Wallace independently worked out the theory of natural selection as an explanation of the "how" of evolution, and in some ways his path toward this solution is easier to follow than Darwin's. Furthermore, he precipitated the long-delayed publication of Darwin's book *On the Origin of Species* by sending an outline of the theory to Darwin in 1858.

It was Bates's good fortune to come upon a marvelous example of the action of natural selection among the butterflies of the Amazon Basin. One of the difficulties in demonstrating evolution by means of natural selection is the length of time required for it to become apparent. But in "Batesian mimicry," the superficial resemblance of a rare palatable butterfly to a common unpalatable butterfly, one can see how natural selection works. The first, good-tasting butterfly is protected from being eaten by birds by its similarity to the second, bad-tasting one. Those butterflies less similar to the bad-tasting ones are quickly

eaten; those more similar are protected—"selected"—
and survive to reproduce their kind.

These principles were discovered by people of
inquiring minds through field work, observation, and
reading, and not in laboratories, although laboratory
work has since added many more details. Underlying
these principles is the great theme of the unity of nature in which plants and animals are simply different
parts of one system, a system of which man is also a
part.

Wallace and Bates belong to that small group of
unusual men who succeed in their endeavors against
great odds. Who were these "determined" young
men? How did they happen on their interest in natural history, and what drew them to the problems of
evolution and the origin of species? What led them
to undertake their long, lonely, and dangerous explorations of the almost unknown tropical regions of the
world? And finally, how did their travels contribute to
the development of their scientific ideas?

Alfred Russel Wallace, the eighth child of
Thomas and Mary Anne Wallace, was born January
8, 1823, in the remote village of Usk in southern
Wales. His father had failed in one financial venture
after another, and the family had moved farther and
farther into the country, where living was cheaper.
When Alfred was five, they made another move, this
time to Hertford, some twenty miles north of London, and here they remained for the next eight or
nine years.

In spite of the family's straitened circumstances,
Alfred looked back on his childhood with pleasure.
He remembered particularly the books read aloud by

his father. These were received from a book club to which his father belonged or borrowed from a small library of which his father became librarian. They were of all kinds, but travel books and biographies were especial favorites.

Alfréd received all his schooling, "a very ordinary education," at the Hertford Grammar School. It included English, Latin, some mathematics, and geography and history, the latter two being merely dull lists of names and dates. During his last year, Alfred assisted in the teaching, probably to help pay the tuition. He found this anomalous position, half teacher and half student, very painful, and he was glad when it came to an end.

This it soon did, for he left school at Christmas in 1836, just before his fourteenth birthday. Like his brothers, he now had to make his own way in the world with little or no help from his parents. But he did not complain about the family's impecunious lot. On the contrary, he later believed that if his father had been more successful, he would himself have accomplished less.

Alfred's prospects seemed quite indifferent, however, when he left home to join his eldest brother, William, to learn surveying. Nevertheless the next few years, to outward appearances so quiet and uneventful, were to determine the course of Alfred's life and to lead him into the company of the greatest scientific figures of his day.

Off and on during the next ten years Alfred worked at surveying. William, fourteen years older, had been well trained as a surveyor and builder. But he had started his career several years before the boom in surveying brought on by the construction of railroads, and jobs were scarce and hard to find. The life was a lonely, wandering one, taking them north of London to the Midlands and to Wales.

With little to occupy him, Alfred turned to the study of natural history. William had already introduced him to geology, some knowledge of which is absorbed by surveyors, and now:

. . . during my solitary rambles I first began to feel the influence of nature and to wish to know more of the various flowers, shrubs, and trees I daily met with, but of which for the most part I did not even know the English names. At that time I hardly realized that there was such a science as systematic botany, that every flower and every meanest and insignificant weed had been accurately described and classified, and that there was any kind of system or order in the endless variety of plants and animals which I knew existed.

This wish to know the names of wild plants, to be able even to speak of them and to learn anything that was known about them, had arisen from a chance remark I had overheard about a year before . . . "we found quite a rarity the other day—a *Monotropa* [a relative of our Indian pipe] ; it has not been found here before." This I pondered over, and wondered what *Monotropa* was. All my father could tell me was that it was a rare plant; and I thought how nice it must be to know the names of rare plants when you found them. However, as I did not even know there were books that described every British plant, and as my brother appeared to take no interest in native plants or animals, except as fossils, nothing came of this desire for knowledge till a few years later.

Alfred was eighteen before he really "discovered" botany in 1841. He and William were then living in the town of Neath in southern Wales. Surveying jobs were scarcer than ever, and Alfred had a good deal of time on his hands.

> But what occupied me chiefly and became more and more the solace and delight of my lonely rambles among the moors and mountains was my first introduction to the variety, the beauty, and the mystery of nature as manifested in the vegetable kingdom.

For one shilling he obtained a copy of a small book on the most common orders of English plants, published by the improbably named Society for Promoting the Diffusion of Useful Knowledge. This became his constant companion on his walks which now more than ever filled him with excitement and delight.

This joy in discovery is one of the keys not only to his future success but also to the charm of his writings on natural history. In fact, it was attendance at a boring lecture on botany that first led Alfred to try his hand at writing in an effort to communicate his own enthusiasm for his new-found pursuit.

William and his parents disapproved of this interest as a waste of time, in spite of the fact that the young surveyor had nothing else to do. And yet the glimpse into this new world was like a magnet drawing him on, and Alfred was not discouraged.

Christmas 1843 marked another turning point for the young Wallace. If he could have made a living at it, he would probably have remained a surveyor, for he enjoyed the work and the outdoor life. But William was again without any jobs, and the younger brother was forced to look for something else. After some searching he found an opening for a junior assistant in the Collegiate School in the midland city of Leicester, and there he taught the younger boys English, reading, writing, and arithmetic, and a bit of surveying and drawing.

It was not the school, however, but the books in the local library and his friendship with an enthusiastic young entomologist, Henry Walter Bates, that changed the course of his life and irrevocably transformed the surveyor into a naturalist.

Bates, two years younger than Wallace, was born in Leicester on February 8, 1825, the eldest son of Henry Bates, a small hosiery manufacturer. His schooling had ended at the same early age as Wallace's, and he was then apprenticed, in 1838, to a hosier in his home town. In spite of the very long hours required by his job, he also enrolled in the evening classes offered by the local Mechanics' Institute, one of many such schools set up to provide technical and scientific training for workingmen. This one had a wide selection of courses, for Bates took Greek, Latin, French, drawing, and composition.

Acquaintances he made at this school introduced Bates to natural history. He was soon absorbed in entomology, the study of insects, collecting first butterflies and then beetles, and enlisting the aid of his younger brothers in the search for specimens. The collection grew quickly. At the same time Bates took

great pains in writing up their many finds, and this
led to his first short scientific paper, written more
than a month before his eighteenth birthday!

Wallace did not recall later how he first met Bates,

> . . . but I rather think I heard him mentioned as
> an enthusiastic entomologist, and met him at the
> library. I found that his specialty was beetle col-
> lecting, though he also had a good set of British
> butterflies. Of the former I had scarcely heard,
> but as I already knew the fascinations of plant
> life I was quite prepared to take an interest in
> any other department of nature.
>
> He asked me to see his collection, and I was
> amazed to find the great number and variety of
> beetles, their many strange forms and often beau-
> tiful markings or coloring, and was even more
> surprised when I found that almost all I saw had
> been collected around Leicester and that there
> were still many more to be discovered. . . . I at
> once determined to begin collecting, as I did not
> find a great many new plants about Leicester.

But collecting, fascinating though it was, was
still not enough for these eager young men. With
amazing discernment they picked out and read some
of the most provocative books of their day—and thus
they came upon that unanswered question, what was
the origin of species? Perhaps their lack of formal
training was a help rather than a hindrance because
their fancies were not so tightly checked by established thinking. In any case their ability to grasp ideas
and to make use of them was remarkable.

One of the most important books of the time

was written not by a biologist, however, but by a political economist. This was the still famous *Essay on the Principle of Population* by Thomas Robert Malthus. First published in 1798, it had already gone through many editions.

Malthus showed that population and food supply increase at different rates. Population increases geometrically, doubling roughly every twenty-five years. Illustrated in numbers, this means multiplying by two in each generation, that is: 2, 4, 8, 16, and so on.

Food supply, on the other hand, increases arithmetically. Using figures again, this means adding two rather than multiplying by two, that is: 2, 4, 6, 8, and so on. The reason for this difference is that the supply of agricultural land is limited, and it is simply not possible to double the amount of it regularly. Of course crop yields have been increased by the use of fertilizer, improved seeds, better farming methods. But the long-term rate of this increase is lower than that for population, and it must result in some conflict, some pressure against the available resources.

According to Malthus, population growth is checked by the resulting vice and misery—starvation, overcrowding, disease, and war. As an economist and also a minister, Malthus' interest was in the unhappy lot of the poor and in the moral perfectibility of man. But he had little hope that the situation would improve unless the people practiced "moral restraint." Otherwise, as conditions improved, the population would increase again, once more reducing the standard of living.

But why did misery and vice exist under a just and benevolent God? Malthus believed that man was by nature indolent and lazy. The difficulties presented by the problems of population were meant to rouse him to work and to improve his mind. He saw a religious purpose in this "struggle for existence," although he had grave doubts about its effectiveness. But Wallace was to see something else—natural selection—not as a planned purpose but as an unplanned result of this struggle in which the best-adapted individuals survived to reproduce their kind.

Another important book was Sir Charles Lyell's *Principles of Geology*. First published in 1830–32, it marked a milestone in the history of geology and indirectly in the history of the theory of evolution as well, although Lyell did not then believe in evolution himself.

Evolution means the gradual change in organisms over a shorter or longer period of time, new species arising from preceding species. But if the world had begun in the year 4004 B.C., as was popularly believed, any changes that had taken place must have occurred within a very short time, a few thousand years at most. Under these circumstances, it seemed reasonable to believe in sudden, overwhelming catastrophies, such as the flood, to account for the observed changes.

Lyell showed, however, that the earth was far older than had been supposed (although he would have been surprised at the current estimates of four and a half billion years). He also pointed out that the same slow geological processes we see operating today, like soil erosion and the action of rivers, operated in the past, that present and past processes were similar. Therefore, the long history of the earth was open to study; it was not completely hidden in the obscurity of sudden and mysterious happenings, as had been thought.

From his study of fossils, Lyell was aware that different species of plants and animals had lived at different times during the earth's long history. But he was unable to account for their appearance other than to suggest that they had been "created" at irregular intervals instead of all at one time. He rejected the solution to this problem proposed by the French naturalist, Jean Baptiste Lamarck, as "the fancied evolution of one species out of another." He added a summary of Lamarck's "theory of the transmutation of species" to his *Principles,* but only to show that he disagreed. Nevertheless this served to introduce it to Wallace and Bates (and also Darwin).

Lamarck believed that animals changed gradually over periods of time, but only as a result of their own individual efforts. Animals caused their own evolution by the use or disuse of particular organs. If the organs were used, they became larger and more powerful; if they were not used because of some change in the habits of an animal, they shrank and finally disappeared. Lastly, these "acquired characteristics" were inherited, resulting in changes in species. Lamarck clearly believed in a theory of evolution, but his mechanism of change worked backward: he thought the changes were caused *by* the living organisms themselves, when really this is something that happens *to* them.

Another suggestion on how evolution could have occurred was published the very year that Wallace moved to Leicester, in Robert Chambers' anonymous book, *Vestiges of the Natural History of Creation.* Chambers wondered why one species could not give birth directly to a next higher one. Why not, if changes as great as from tadpole to frog take place before our eyes? Although such unscientific proposals brought ridicule upon the book, it was nevertheless quite popular outside scientific circles, and it helped to pave the way for the eventual acceptance of the theory of evolution.

Two other books deserve mention here because they drew Wallace's and Bates's attention to the distant continent of South America: Alexander von Humboldt's *Personal Narrative of Travels to the Equinoctial Regions of the New Continent* and Charles Darwin's *Voyage of the Beagle*. Wallace and Bates read these with much interest and enjoyment, but with little thought that such trips might lie in their own futures.

Abruptly and unexpectedly, the happy years in Leicester came to an end. Wallace's brother William died in February 1846, and Wallace returned to Neath to help settle his affairs. The business had picked up with the increase in railway surveying, and Wallace now tried to keep it going with the aid of another brother, John. But he found business details irksome, and he also felt cut off from his interests and friends in Leicester. He kept in touch with Bates, however, who felt equally constrained by his job as a clerk, and in the next few years the two young friends worked out a daring scheme of escape from their humdrum prospects—they would go to South America themselves!

Their interest in South America had been aroused by Darwin and Humboldt. What spurred them to action, however, was the appearance in 1847 of a small "unpretending volume," *A Voyage up the River Amazon, including a Residence at Pará [Belém]*. This was an account by a young American amateur naturalist, William Henry Edwards, of his three-month trip up the Amazon River during the summer of 1846. To amuse himself and, as he wrote, to compensate for "the monsters which did *not* meet his curious eye, he collected as many specimens in different departments of natural history as were in his power."

Fascinated by the apparently limitless possibilities for collecting, Wallace and Bates began seriously to consider whether they might be able to make such a trip. They inquired at the British Museum about its practicality and were assured that anything they might collect in the almost unexplored region of northern Brazil—insects, land shells, birds, or mammals—could easily be sold to museums or private collectors in Europe. This would pay their expenses. And, perhaps somewhat brashly, they also planned to keep duplicate collections for their own study because they hoped now to gather facts "toward solving the problem of the origin of species."

Soon they were deep in preparation for the journey, studying the collections in the British Museum, buying necessary books and equipment, and arranging for an agent to handle the sales of the specimens. By coincidence Edwards himself was in London at the same time, and he gave them further information and introductions to people whom he had met.

At last all was in readiness, and at the end of April 1848 the two young men set sail for South America and their new careers.

part one

The Amazon River Basin

I embarked at Liverpool, with Mr. Wallace, in a small trading vessel, on the 26th of April, 1848; and, after a swift passage from the Irish Channel to the equator, arrived, on the 26th of May, off Salinas. This is the pilot station for vessels bound to Belém, the only port of entry to the vast region watered by the Amazons.

BATES, *Naturalist on the Amazons*

1

THE FOREST

. . . the virgin forest, everywhere grand,
often beautiful and even sublime. Its wonderful variety with a more general uniformity never palled.

WALLACE, *My Life*

■ And so the two young men began their years of
lonely wandering in the tropical wilderness. Wallace
spent four years there (and another eight on the opposite side of the world) and Bates spent eleven,
testament indeed to their stamina and determination.
Besides this, they both succeeded in making important scientific contributions, a remarkable achieve-
ment at any time.

But first of all they settled down on the outskirts
of the small city of Pará, present-day Belém, spending more than a year familiarizing themselves with
their new surroundings before tackling the mighty
Amazon itself. Entirely dependent as they were upon
their own wits and resourcefulness, they had to begin

by learning the local customs and the Portuguese language. Then they could turn their attention to the forest that stretches nearly two thousand miles from the Atlantic Ocean to the Andes Mountains.

Unlike gold seekers or other exploiters, Wallace and Bates met the forest and its inhabitants on their own terms. The two naturalists tried to understand them, not to use them. As a result they lived successfully for years in one of the most difficult regions of the earth, and they unraveled some of the secrets of its natural history.

Time and understanding were two especially important factors in their success. Most modern travelers fly in for short stays and then leave without having had time to comprehend what they have seen. It is Wallace's and Bates's long residence in this still poorly understood part of the world that makes the accounts of their travels so valuable even today.

Wallace had thought he would find the forests abounding in hummingbirds, parrots and monkeys, but he quickly discovered that he had to look in the right places. They were plentiful enough, "but they require looking for, and a certain amount of acquaintance with them is necessary in order to discover their haunts, and some practice is required to see them in the thick forest, even when you hear them close by you." This kind of patient observation is as necessary in temperate as in tropical climes, indeed anywhere, and is the beginning of understanding of any landscape.

At the same time, tropical regions differ in many ways from temperate regions. The differences stem from some special characteristics of the tropics, situated as they are on either side of the equator. To begin

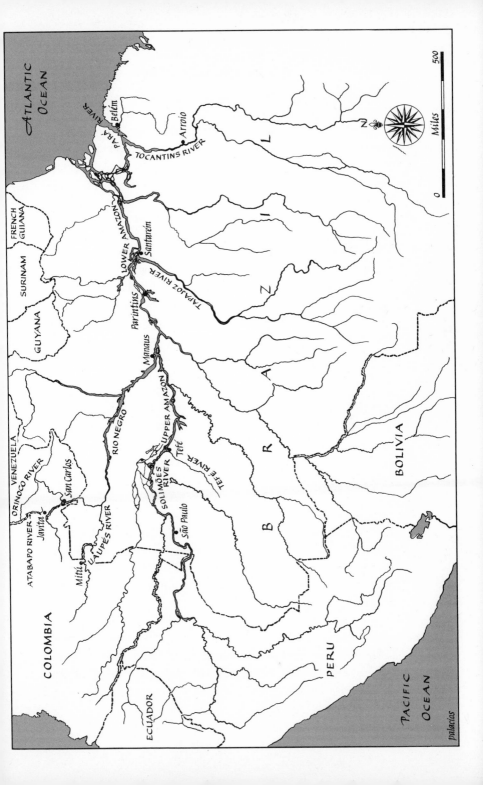

with, the days and nights are of about equal length throughout the year. The climate does not show the seasonal variation to which northerners are accustomed—spring, summer, fall, and winter. Instead the temperature remains high all year round, and the seasonal changes depend on differences in the amount of rainfall.

The tropical rain forest also differs from forests of temperate and northern regions in its great age. The Amazonian forest has existed relatively undisturbed for over one hundred million years. It was not overrun by the glaciers of the Ice Age, nor was it even inhabited by man until a few thousand years ago. In contrast, the forests of the northern United States and Canada date only from about eleven thousand years ago, when the ice melted at the end of the last glacial period.

One result of these differences is the enormous number of species of plants and animals (principally insects) to be found in tropical regions compared with the much smaller number to be found in northern regions. On the other hand, the number of individuals of any one species is usually very small and quite locally distributed.

The extraordinary abundance of species can be seen from Wallace's report of their first two months of collecting: "the large number of 553 species of Lepidoptera (of which more than 400 were butterflies), 450 beetles, and 400 of other orders, making in all 1300 species of insects."

And except for palms, tropical trees are not found in large stands of one kind, as we might expect. Instead there may be as many as a hundred different species in one acre, and even a common species may occur only once in five acres. Lumbering, consequently, is quite a different matter in the tropics from what it is in the north.

Another striking characteristic of the tropical forest is the number of arboreal or climbing species of both plants and animals. Most noticeable, of course, is the forest itself, with its canopy of flowers and fruits often a hundred or more feet above the ground. Sunlight is necessary for photosynthesis, and the light above the canopy is some twenty-five times stronger than it is on the dim forest floor far below. Plants, therefore, must climb to live.

Many of the plants are epiphytes, or air plants, which simply use the stronger trees for support, thus getting high enough to survive. They obtain necessary moisture from the moisture-laden air. Other plants are rooted, but they also use large trees for support, climbing and twisting their way upward.

The animals also climb, although except for the noisy and conspicuous monkeys, mammals are generally scarce in the forest. There are climbing species of such mammals as sloths and anteaters and, of course, of members of the cat family. Much more common, however, are the numerous species of arboreal beetles. And even birds that in other parts of the world would normally be found on the ground are here adapted to living in trees.

The Amazon Basin is often thought of as one of the few areas in the world that is still available for agricultural exploitation. But this is true only in a limited sense, for tree crops suited to tropical conditions.

Wallace (and Bates) mistakenly thought that the forest could easily be converted into "rich pasture and meadow land, into cultivated fields, gardens, and orchards," and they deplored the primitive Indian methods. And yet the typical mandioca field that Wallace described is actually much better suited to the conditions of a tropical rain forest.

Tropical soil is unstable, and it quickly loses its fertility when exposed to the action of the burning sun and drenching rains. Furthermore, the common lateritic soils of the tropics, which are rich in iron and alumina, may become hard as a brick—the word "laterite" comes from *later*, the Latin word for brick or tile—when they are no longer protected by their forest cover, and there is no known way of reversing this. It may take from five hundred to a thousand years for the forest to replace itself in a clearing even as small as ten acres, if it is possible at all. This may be one reason that advanced civilizations have not survived in tropical regions.

There are other reasons why the forest should be protected from careless cutting. The heavy rainfall is itself dependent on the moisture-laden air above the forests. Today there is some concern that cutting them down is leading to a reduction in rainfall there. Furthermore, people and animals require oxygen to live, and much of the world's supply is made available to them through the photosynthetic activity of tropical forests. Forests have an important role to play in the natural economy of the earth, and their fate is a matter of concern to everyone.

THE TROPICAL RAIN FOREST

[WALLACE] Perhaps no country in the world contains such an amount of vegetable matter on its surface as

the valley of the Amazon. Its entire extent, with the
exception of some very small portions, is covered with
one dense and lofty primeval forest, the most extensive and unbroken which exists upon the earth. It is
the great feature of the country—that which at once
stamps it as a unique and peculiar region. It is not
here as on the coasts of southern Brazil or on the
shores of the Pacific, where a few days' journey
suffices to carry us beyond the forest district and into
the parched plains and rocky *serras* [mountain
ranges] of the interior. Here we may travel for weeks
and months inland in any direction and find scarcely
an acre of ground unoccupied by trees. It is far up in
the interior, where the great mass of this mighty forest is found; not on the lower part of the river, near
the coast, as is generally supposed. . . .

For the first thousand miles . . . the width of
the forest from north to south is about four hundred
miles. It then stretches out both to the north and
south so that . . . it extends from . . . the banks
of the Orinoco to . . . the northern slope of the Andes of Bolivia, a distance of more than seventeen
hundred miles. . . .

The forests of no other part of the world are so
extensive and unbroken as this. Those of Central Europe are trifling in comparison; nor in India are they
very continuous or extensive; while the rest of Asia
seems to be a country of thinly wooded plains and
steppes and deserts. Africa contains some large forests, situated on the east and west coasts and in the
interior south of the equator, but the whole of them
would bear but a small proportion to that of the Amazon. In North America alone is there anything approaching to it, where the whole country east of the

Mississippi and about the great lakes is, or has been, an almost uninterrupted extent of woodland.

In a general survey of the earth, we may therefore look upon the New World as preeminently the land of forests, contrasting strongly with the old, where steppes and deserts are the most characteristic features. . . .

The forests of the Amazon are distinguished from those of most other countries by the great variety of species of trees composing them. Instead of extensive tracts covered with pines or oaks or beeches, we scarcely ever see two individuals of the same species together, except in certain cases, principally among the palms. . . . Generally, however, the same species of tree is repeated only at distant intervals. . . .

Certain kinds of hardwoods are used on the Amazon and Rio Negro for the construction of canoes and the schooners used in the navigation of the river. The difficulty of getting timber of any one kind for these vessels is so great that they are often constructed of half a dozen different sorts of wood, and not always of the same colors or degrees of hardness. Trees producing fruit, or with medicinal properties, are often so widely scattered that two or three only are found within a reasonable distance of a village, and supply the whole population. This peculiarity of distribution must prevent a great trade in timber for any particular purpose being carried on here. The India rubber and Brazil nut trees are not altogether exceptions to this rule, and the produce from them is collected over an immense extent of country, to which the innumerable lakes and streams offer a ready access. . . .

There is a grandeur and solemnity in the tropical forest, but little of beauty or brilliancy of color. The huge buttress trees, the fissured trunks, the extraordinary air roots, the twisted and wrinkled climbers, and the elegant palms are what strike the attention and fill the mind with admiration and surprise and awe. But all is gloomy and solemn, and one feels a relief on again seeing the blue sky and feeling the scorching rays of the sun.

It is on the roadside and on the rivers' banks that we see all the beauty of the tropical vegetation. There we find a mass of bushes and shrubs and trees of every height, rising over one another, all exposed to the bright light and the fresh air; and putting forth, within reach, their flowers and fruit, which, in the forest, only grow far up on the topmost branches. Bright flowers and green foliage combine their charms, and climbers with their flowery festoons cover over the bare and decaying stems. . . .

What we may fairly allow of tropical vegetation is that there is a much greater number of species, and a greater variety of forms, than in the temperate zones. Among this great variety occur, as we might reasonably expect, the most striking and brilliant flowers, and the most remarkable forms of stem and foliage. But there is no evidence to show that the proportion of species bearing brightly colored compared to those bearing inconspicuous flowers is any greater in the tropics than in the temperate regions. And with regard to individuals—which is, after all, what produces the effects of vegetation—it seems probable that there is a greater mass of brilliant coloring and picturesque beauty produced by plants in the temperate than in the tropical regions.

On the morning of the 23rd of June we started
early to walk to the rice mills at Maguarí. . . . At
about two miles from the city we entered the virgin
forest, which the increased height of the trees and the
deeper shade had some time told us we were approaching. Its striking characteristics were the great
number and variety of the forest trees, their trunks
rising frequently for sixty or eighty feet without a
branch, and perfectly straight; the huge creepers
which climb about them, sometimes stretching
obliquely from their summits like the stays of a mast,
sometimes winding around their trunks like immense
serpents waiting for their prey. . . .

Among the trees the various kinds that have buttresses projecting around their base are the most striking and peculiar. Some of these buttresses are much
longer than they are high, springing from a distance
of eight or ten feet from the base and reaching only
four or five feet high on the trunk, while others rise
to the height of twenty or thirty feet. . . .

The stems of all these trees, and the climbers
that wind or wave around them, support a multitude
of dependents. Tillandsias and other bromeliads, resembling wild pineapples, large climbing arums, with
their dark green arrowhead-shaped leaves, peppers in
great variety, and large-leaved ferns shoot out at intervals all up the stem, to the very topmost branches. Between these, creeping ferns and delicate little species
like our *Hymenophyllum* abound, and in moist dark
places the leaves of these are again covered with minute
creeping mosses and hepaticas—so that we have parasites on parasites, and on these parasites again. On
looking upward, the finely divided foliage, strongly defined against the clear sky, is a striking characteristic

of the tropical forests, as is repeatedly remarked by Humboldt. Many of the largest forest trees have leaves as delicate as those of the trembling *Mimosa*. . . .

[BATES] We often read in books of travels of the silence and gloom of the Brazilian forests. They are realities, and the impression deepens on a longer acquaintance. The few sounds of birds are of that pensive or mysterious character which intensifies the feeling of solitude rather than imparts a sense of life and cheerfulness.

Sometimes, in the midst of the stillness, a sudden yell or scream will startle one; this comes from some defenseless fruit-eating animal, which is pounced upon by a tiger cat or stealthy boa constrictor. Morning and evening the howling monkeys make a most fearful and harrowing noise under which it is difficult to keep up one's buoyancy of spirit. The feeling of inhospitable wildness which the forest is calculated to inspire is increased tenfold under this fearful uproar. Often, even in the still hours of midday, a sudden crash will be heard resounding afar through the wilderness as some great bough or entire tree falls to the ground.

There are, besides, many sounds which it is impossible to account for. I found the natives generally as much at a loss in this respect as myself. Sometimes a sound is heard like the clang of an iron bar against a hard, hollow tree, or a piercing cry rends the air; these are not repeated, and the succeeding silence tends to heighten the unpleasant impression which they make on the mind. With the natives it is always the *curupira*, the wild man or spirit of the forest, which produces all noises they are unable to explain.

NATIVE AGRICULTURE

[WALLACE] . . . farina, rice, salt-fish, and fruits are the principal food of the Indians and Negroes. Farina is a preparation from the root of the mandioca, or cassava, plant, of which tapioca is also made. It looks something like coarsely ground peas, or perhaps more like sawdust, and when soaked in water or broth is rather glutinous, and is a very nutritious article of food. . . .

Proceeding onward, we came to another recently cleared mandioca field. Here the path was quite obliterated, and we had to cross over it as we could. Imagine the trees of a virgin forest cut down so as to fall across each other in every conceivable direction. After lying a few months they are burned; the fire, however, only consumes the leaves and fine twigs and branches; all the rest remains entire, but blackened and charred. The mandioca is then planted without any further preparation; and it was across such a field that we, all heavily laden, had to find our way. Now climbing on the top of some huge trunk, now walking over a shaking branch or creeping among a confused thicket of charcoal, few journeys require more equanimity of temper than one across an Amazonian clearing.

FLOWERING TREES

The vegetation improved in appearance as the dry season advanced. Plants were successively budding and bursting their blossoms, and bright green leaves displaced the half-withered ones of the past season. The climbers were particularly remarkable, as much for the beauty of their foliage as for their flowers. . . . A few forest trees were also in blossom, and it was truly a magnificent sight to behold a great tree covered with one mass of flowers and to hear the deep distant hum of millions of insects gathered together to enjoy the honeyed feast.

But all is out of reach of the curious and admiring naturalist. It is only over the outside of the great dome of verdure exposed to the vertical rays of the sun that flowers are produced, and on many of these trees there is not a single blossom to be found at a less height than a hundred feet. The whole glory of these forests could only be seen by sailing gently in a balloon over the undulating flowery surface above; such a treat is perhaps reserved for the traveler of a future age.

MONKEYS

But to me the greatest treat was making my first acquaintance with the monkeys. One morning, when walking alone in the forest, I heard a rustling of the leaves and branches, as if a man were walking quickly among them and expected every minute to see some Indian hunter make his appearance, when all at once the sounds appeared to be in the branches above, and turning up my eyes there, I saw a large monkey looking down at me, and seeming as much astonished as I was myself. I should have liked to have had a good look at him, but he thought it safer to retreat.

The next day, being out with Mr. Leavens near the same place, we heard a similar sound, and it was soon evident that a whole troop of monkeys were approaching. We therefore hid ourselves under some trees, and with guns cocked, waited their coming. Presently we caught a glimpse of them skipping about among the trees, leaping from branch to branch and passing from one tree to another with the greatest ease. At last one approached too near for its safety. Mr. Leavens fired, and it fell, the rest making off with all possible speed. The poor little animal was not quite dead, and its cries, its innocent-looking countenance, and delicate little hands were quite childlike.

Having often heard how good monkey was, I took it home and had it cut up and fried for breakfast. There was about as much of it as a fowl, and the meat something resembled rabbit, without any very peculiar or unpleasant flavor.

THE CLIMBING HABITS OF PLANTS AND ANIMALS

[BATES] The woods were at first of recent growth, dense, and utterly impenetrable; the ground, instead of being clothed with grass and shrubs as in the woods of Europe, was everywhere carpeted with lycopodiums (fern-shaped mosses). Gradually the scene changed. We descended slightly from an elevated, dry, and sandy area to a low swampy one; a cool air breathed on our faces and a moldy smell of rotting vegetation greeted us. The trees were now taller, the underwood less dense, and we could obtain glimpses into the wilderness on all sides. The leafy crowns of the trees, scarcely two of which could be seen together of the same kind, were now far away above us, in another world as it were. We could only see at times, where there was a break above, the tracery of the foliage against the clear blue sky. Sometimes the leaves were palmate, or of the shape of large outstretched hands; at others, finely cut or feathery, like the leaves of mimosas.

Below, the tree trunks were everywhere linked together by *cipós*, the woody, flexible stems of climbing and creeping trees whose foliage is far away above, mingled with that of the taller independent trees. Some were twisted in strands like cables, others had thick stems contorted in every variety of shape, entwining snakelike round the tree trunks or forming gigantic loops and coils among the larger branches; others, again, were of zigzag shape, or indented like the steps of a staircase, sweeping from the ground to a giddy height.

It interested me much afterward to find that these climbing trees do not form any particular family. There is no distinct group of plants whose especial habit is to climb, but species of many and the most diverse families, the bulk of whose members are not climbers, seem to have been driven by circumstances to adopt this habit. There is even a climbing genus of palms (*Desmoncus*), the species of which are called, in the Tupi language, *jacitara*. These have slender, thickly spined, and flexuous stems which twine about the taller trees from one to the other and grow to an incredible length. The leaves, which have the ordinary pinnate shape characteristic of the family, are emitted from the stems at long intervals instead of being collected into a dense crown, and have at their tips a number of long recurved spines. These structures are excellent contrivances to enable the trees to secure themselves by in climbing, but they are a great nuisance to the traveler, for they sometimes hang over the pathway and catch the hat or clothes, dragging off the one or tearing the other as he passes. The number and variety of climbing trees in the Amazon forests are interesting, taken in connection with the fact of the very general tendency of the animals also to become climbers.

All the Amazonian, and in fact all South American, monkeys are climbers. There is no group answering to the baboons of the Old World, which live on the ground. The gallinaceous birds of the country, the representatives of the fowls and pheasants of Asia and Africa, are all adapted by the position of the toes to perch on trees, and it is only on trees, at a great height, that they are to be seen. A genus allied to the bears (*Potos,* the kinkajou), found only in the Amazonian forests, is entirely arboreal and has a long flexible tail like that of certain monkeys.

Many other similar instances could be enumerated, but I will mention only the carnivorous ground beetles, a great proportion of whose genera and species in these forest regions are, by the structure of their feet, fitted to live exclusively on the branches and leaves of trees.

COLLECTING IN THE FOREST

We now settled ourselves for a few months' regular work. We had the forest on three sides of us; it was the end of the wet season; most species of birds had finished molting and every day the insects increased in number and variety. Behind the *rocinha* [country house] after several days' exploration, I found a series of pathways through the woods, which led to the Una road. . . . The paths hereabout were very productive of insects, and being entirely under shade, were very pleasant for strolling. Close to our doors began the main forest road. It was broad enough for two horsemen abreast and branched off in three directions, the main line going to the village of Ourém, a distance of fifty miles. This road formerly extended to São Lúiz de Maranhão, but it had been long in disuse and was now grown up, being scarcely passable between Belém and Ourém.

Our researches were made in various directions along these paths, and every day produced us a number of new and interesting species. Collecting, preparing our specimens, and making notes kept us well occupied. One day was so much like another that a general description of the diurnal round of incidents, including the sequence of natural phenomena, will be sufficient to give an idea of how days pass to naturalists under the equator.

We used to rise soon after dawn when Isidoro [the cook] would go down to the city, after supplying us with a cup of coffee, to purchase the fresh provisions for the day. The two hours before breakfast were devoted to ornithology. At that early period of the day the sky was invariably cloudless (the thermometer marking 72 degrees or 73 degrees Fahrenheit; the heavy dew or the previous night's rain, which lay on the moist foliage, becoming quickly dissipated by the glowing sun, which rising straight out of the east, mounted rapidly toward the zenith. All nature was fresh, new leaf and flower buds expanding rapidly. Some mornings a single tree would appear in flower amidst what was the preceding evening a uniform green mass of forest—a dome of blossom suddenly created as if by magic. The birds were all active; from the wild fruit trees not far off we often heard the shrill yelping of the toucans (*Ramphastos vitellinus*). Small flocks of parrots flew over on most mornings at a great height, appearing in distinct relief against the blue sky, always two by two, chattering to each other, the pairs being separated by regular intervals; their bright colors, however, were not apparent at that height. After breakfast we devoted the hours from 10:00 A.M. to 2:00 or 3:00 P.M. to entomology, the best time for insects in the forest being a little before the greatest heat of the day.

The heat increased rapidly toward two o'clock (92 degrees and 93 degrees Fahrenheit), by which time every voice of bird or mammal was hushed, only in the trees was heard at intervals the harsh whirr of a cicada. The leaves, which were so moist and fresh in early morning, now become lax and drooping, the flowers shed their petals. Our neighbors, the Indian and mulatto inhabitants of the open palm-thatched huts, as we returned home fatigued with our ramble, were either asleep in their hammocks or seated on mats in the shade, too languid even to talk.

On most days in June and July a heavy shower would fall some time in the afternoon, producing a most welcome coolness. The approach of the rain clouds was after a uniform fashion very interesting to observe. First, the cool sea breeze, which commenced to blow about ten o'clock and which had increased in

force with the increasing power of the sun, would flag
and finally die away. The heat and electric tension of
the atmosphere would then become almost insupportable. Languor and uneasiness would seize on every
one, even the denizens of the forest betraying it by
their motions. White clouds would appear in the east
and gather into cumuli, with an increasing blackness
along their lower portions. The whole eastern horizon
would become almost suddenly black, and this would
spread upward, the sun at length becoming obscured.
Then the rush of a mighty wind is heard through the
forest, swaying the tree tops; a vivid flash of lightning
bursts forth, then a crash of thunder, and down
streams the deluging rain. Such storms soon cease,
leaving bluish-black motionless clouds in the sky until
night. Meanwhile all nature is refreshed, but heaps of
flower petals and fallen leaves are seen under the
trees.

Toward evening life revives again and the ring-
ing uproar is resumed from bush and tree. The following morning the sun again rises in the cloudless
sky, and so the cycle is completed: spring, summer,
and autumn, as it were, in one tropical day. The days
are more or less like this throughout the year in this
country.

A little difference exists between the dry and wet
seasons, but generally the dry season, which lasts
from July to December, is varied with showers, and
the wet, from January to June, with sunny days. It re-
sults from this that the periodical phenomena of
plants and animals do not take place at about the
same time in all species, or in the individuals of any
given species, as they do in temperate countries. Of
course there is no hibernation, nor, as the dry season

is not excessive, is there any summer torpidity as in some tropical countries. Plants do not flower or shed their leaves, nor do birds molt, pair, or breed simultaneously.

In Europe a woodland scene has its spring, its summer, its autumnal, and its winter aspects. In the equatorial forests the aspect is the same or nearly so every day in the year: budding, flowering, fruiting, and leaf shedding are always going on in one species or other. The activity of birds and insects proceeds without interruption, each species having its own separate times. The colonies of wasps, for instance, do not die off annually, leaving only the queens, as in cold climates, but the succession of generations and colonies goes on incessantly.

It is never either spring, summer, or autumn, but each day is a combination of all three. With the day and night always of equal length, the atmospheric disturbances of each day neutralizing themselves before each succeeding morn, with the sun in its course proceeding midway across the sky and the daily temperature the same within two or three degrees throughout the year—how grand in its perfect equilibrium and simplicity is the march of nature under the equator!

Our evenings were generally fully employed preserving our collections and making notes. We dined at four and took tea about seven o'clock. Sometimes we walked to the city to see Brazilian life or enjoy the pleasures of European and American society.

2

THE RIVERS

The night was transparently clear and almost cold, the moon appeared sharply defined against the dark blue sky, and a ridge of foam marked where the prow of the vessel was cleaving its way through the water. The men had made a fire in the galley to make tea of an acid herb called *erva cidreira*, a quantity of which they had gathered at the last landing place, and the flames sparkled cheerily upward. It is at such times as these that Amazon traveling is enjoyable, and one no longer wonders at the love which many, both natives and strangers, have for this wandering life.

BATES, *Naturalist on the Amazons*

■The rivers are the second dominating feature of the Amazon region. So large is this river system, in fact, that one-fifth of the total fresh water in the world flows through it. Naturally enough, Wallace and Bates found that most transportation was by water, and the local people were, as Bates called them, semiaquatic. Roads and paths through the dense forest were a rarity anyway, in this thinly populated area.

Their first excursions were to some nearby mills to whose manager, a Mr. Leavens, Edwards had given them an introduction. Leavens then invited them to accompany him on a trip up the River Tocantins, a large tributary of the Amazon from the south.

Like many other tributaries of the Amazon, this one was easily navigable for only a little over a hundred miles. Then began a series of rocky waterfalls or cataracts, dangerous in the dry season and even more so in the wet. Bates never attempted to pass such falls, but Wallace later made some extremely hazardous ascents of the Rio Negro and its smaller tributary the River Uaupés.

They returned to Belém from the Tocantins at the end of September 1848. From then until the beginning of the next dry season, the two young naturalists explored the neighborhood of Belém independently.

In July 1849 Wallace's youngest brother, Herbert, arrived from England to try his hand at collecting, and in early August the two brothers set off on the long-awaited trip up the Amazon. Their first goal was Santarém, five hundred miles inland, and from there they traveled on to Barra (present-day Manaus) at the mouth of the Rio Negro, a thousand miles from the sea.

Bates made his way up the Amazon separately, starting in early September. He arrived at Manaus in January 1850, three weeks after the Wallaces. Here, after they had rested, they "arranged for further explorations in the interior of the country. Mr. Wallace chose the Rio Negro for his next trip, and I agreed to take the Solimões. . . ."

The Rio Negro flows south from Venezuela, and then east and south in Brazil toward the Amazon; the Uaupés joins it from the west, part way down. The thirty miles of falls on the lower Rio Negro were dwarfed in difficulty by those on the Uaupés. Not surprisingly, his four-hundred-mile journey up the Uaupés brought Wallace into "country that no European traveler had ever before visited." Despite the falls, illness, and inadequate equipment, he was determined to survey these rivers, and he succeeded during the course of two trips in making a very creditable map.

Bates also made two trips to the Solimões, or Upper Amazon. The first year at Tefé, some four hundred miles beyond Manaus, was filled with hardships, and he reluctantly decided to give up the whole project. Returning to Belém in April 1851, he met Herbert Wallace, who was also planning to go back to England. But the city was then in the grip of smallpox and yellow fever epidemics, and both men caught yellow fever. Herbert unfortunately died, but Bates was lucky and recovered.

Now, encouraged by letters and money from home, Bates decided to retrace his steps up the Amazon, studying at greater leisure some of the more interesting places he had passed. He spent nearly four more years on the Lower Amazon exploring Santarém and the Tapajoz River and other nearby places, and then yet another four years on the Upper Amazon, with his headquarters again at Tefé.

TRAVELING ON RIVERS
AND CANOE PATHS

[BATES] The creek Iritirí at the mills [near Belém] is only a few yards wide; it winds about between two lofty walls of forest for some distance, then becomes much broader, and finally joins the Maguarí. . . .

We made many excursions down the Iritirí and saw much of these creeks; besides, our second visit to the mills was by water. The Maguarí is a magnificent channel; the different branches form quite a labyrinth, and the land is everywhere of little elevation. All these smaller rivers throughout the Pará estuary are of the nature of creeks. The land is so level that the short local rivers have no sources and downward currents like rivers as we generally understand them. They serve the purpose of draining the land, but instead of having a constant current one way, they have a regular ebb and flow with the tide. The natives call them, in the Tupi language, *igarapés,* or canoe paths.

The igarapés and *furos,* or channels, which are infinite in number in this great river delta, are characteristic of the country. The land is everywhere covered with impenetrable forests; the houses and villages are all on the waterside, and nearly all communication is by water. This semiaquatic life of the people is one of the most interesting features of the country.

For short excursions, and for fishing in still waters, a small boat called *montaria* is universally used. It is made of five planks—a broad one for the bottom, bent into the proper shape by the action of heat, two narrow ones for the sides, and two small trianguglar pieces for stem and stern. It has no rudder; the paddle serves for both steering and propelling. The montaria takes here the place of the horse, mule, or camel of other regions.

Besides one or more montarias, almost every

family has a larger canoe called *igarité*. This is fitted with two masts, a rudder, and keel, and has an arched awning or cabin near the stern, made of a framework of tough lianas, thatched with palm leaves. In the igarité they will cross stormy rivers fifteen or twenty miles broad. The natives are all boat builders. It is often remarked by white residents that an Indian is a carpenter and shipwright by intuition.

It is astonishing to see in what crazy vessels these people will risk themselves. I have seen Indians cross rivers in a leaky montaria when it required the nicest equilibrium to keep the leak just above the water; a movement of a hairsbreadth would send all to the bottom, but they managed to cross in safety. They are especially careful when they have strangers under their charge, and it is the custom of Brazilian and Portuguese travelers to leave the whole management to them. When they are alone they are more reckless, and often have to swim for their lives. If a squall overtakes them as they are crossing in a heavily laden canoe, they all jump overboard and swim about until the heavy sea subsides, when they reembark.

THE RIVER TOCANTINS

Mr. Wallace and I started today [Aug. 26, 1848] on the excursion which I have already mentioned as having been planned with Mr. Leavens, up the river Tocantins, whose mouth lies about forty-five miles in a straight line, but eighty miles following the bends of the river channels, to the southwest of Belém. This river . . . has a course of sixteen hundred miles, and stands third in rank amongst the streams which form the Amazon system.

The preparations for the journey took a great deal of time and trouble. We had first to hire a proper vessel, a two-masted *vigilenga* twenty-seven feet long, with a flat prow and great breadth of beam and fitted to live in heavy seas; for although our voyage was only a river trip, there were vast sealike expanses of water to traverse. It was not decked over, but had two arched awnings formed of strong wickerwork, and thatched with palm leaves. We had then to store it with provisions for three months, the time we at first intended to be away; procure the necessary passports; and, lastly, engage a crew.

Mr. Leavens, having had much experience in the country, managed all these matters. He brought two Indians from the rice mills, and these induced another to enroll himself. We, on our parts, took our cook Isidoro and a young Indian lad named Antonio who had attached himself to us in the course of our residence at Nazareth [then a small village on the outskirts of Belém].

Our principal man was Alexandro, one of Mr. Leavens' Indians. He was an intelligent and well-disposed young Tapuyo, an expert sailor and an indefatigable hunter. To his fidelity we were indebted for being enabled to carry out any of the objects of our voyage. Being a native of a district near the capital, Alexandro was a civilized Tapuyo, a citizen as free as his white neighbors. He spoke only Portuguese. . . . I esteemed him as a quiet, sensible, manly young fellow.

. . . We were now well out of the low alluvial country of the Amazon proper, and the climate was

evidently much drier than it is near Belém. They had
had no rain here for many weeks. . . .

The next day before sunrise a fine breeze sprang
up and the men awoke and set the sails. We glided all
day through channels between islands with long,
white sandy beaches, over which, now and then,
aquatic and wading birds were seen running. The forest was low and had a harsh, dry aspect. Several palm
trees grew here which we had not before seen. On
low bushes near the water, pretty, red-capped cardi-
nals (*Paroaria gularis*) were numerous, flitting about
and chirping like sparrows.

About half past four P.M., we brought to at the
mouth of a creek or channel where there was a great
extent of sandy beach. The sand had been blown by
the wind into ridges and undulations, and over the
moister parts large flocks of sandpipers were running
about.

Alexandro and I had a long ramble over the rolling plain, which came as an agreeable change after
the monotonous forest scenery amid which we had
been so long traveling. He pointed out to me the
tracks of a huge jaguar on the sand. We found here
also our first turtle's nest, and obtained one hundred
twenty eggs from it, which were laid at a depth of
nearly two feet from the surface, the mother first ex-
cavating a hole, and afterward covering it up with
sand. The place is discoverable only by following the
tracks of the turtle from the water. I saw here an alligator for the first time, which reared its head and
shoulders above the water just after I had taken a
bath near the spot. The night was calm and cloudless,
and we employed the hours before bedtime in an-
gling by moonlight.

THE CATARACTS NEAR ARROIO

We arrived at Arroio about four o'clock in the afternoon, after ten hours' hard pull. The place consists simply of a few houses built on a high bank, and forms a station where canoemen from the mining countries of the interior of Brazil stop to rest themselves before or after surmounting the dreaded falls and rapids of Guaribas, situated a couple of miles farther up.

We dined ashore, and in the evening again embarked to visit the falls. The vigorous and successful way in which our men battled with the terrific currents excited our astonishment. The bed of the river, here about a mile wide, is strewn with blocks of various sizes which lie in the most irregular manner, and between them rush currents of more or less rapidity. With an accurate knowledge of the place and skillful management, the falls can be approached in small canoes by threading the less dangerous channels.

The main falls is about a quarter of a mile wide; we climbed to an elevation overlooking it and had a good view of the cataract. A body of water rushes with terrific force down a steep slope, and boils up with deafening roar around the boulders which obstruct its course. The wildness of the whole scene was very impressive. As far as the eye could reach, stretched range after range of wooded hills, scores of miles of beautiful wilderness, inhabited only by scanty tribes of wild Indians. In the midst of such a solitude the roar of the cataract seemed fitting music.

We commenced early in the morning our downward voyage. Arroio is situated in about latitude 4 degrees 10 minutes south, and lies therefore about one hundred thirty miles from the mouth of the Tocantins. Fifteen miles above Guaribas another similar cataract called Tabocas lies across the river. We were told that there were in all fifteen of these obstructions to navigation between Arroio and the mouth of the Araguaya. The worst was the Inferno, the Guaribas standing second to it in evil reputation. Many canoes and lives have been lost here, most of the accidents arising through the vessels being hurled against an enormous cubical mass of rock called the Guaribinha, which we, on our trip to the falls in the small canoe, passed round with the greatest ease about a quarter of a mile below the main falls. This, however, was the dry season; in the time of full waters a tremendous current sets against it. We descended the river rapidly, and found it excellent fun shooting the rapids. The men seemed to delight in choosing the swiftest parts of the current; they sang and yelled in the greatest excitement, working the paddles with great force and throwing clouds of spray above us as we bounded downward. . . .

In descending the river we landed frequently, and Mr. Wallace and I lost no chance of adding to our collections, so that before the end of our journey we had got together a very considerable number of birds, insects, and shells. . . .

EARLY TRAVELERS ON THE AMAZON

At the time of my first voyage up the Amazon— namely in 1849—nearly all communication with the interior was by means of small sailing vessels owned by traders residing in the remote towns and villages, who seldom came to Belém themselves, but entrusted vessels and cargoes to the care of half-breeds or Portuguese *cabos* [captains]. Sometimes, indeed, they risked all in the hands of the Indian crew, making the pilot, who was also steersman, do duty as supercargo.

Now and then Portuguese and Brazilian merchants at Belém furnished young Portuguese with merchandise and dispatched them to the interior to exchange the goods for produce among the scattered population. The means of communication, in fact, with the upper parts of the Amazon had been on the decrease for some time on account of the augmented difficulty of obtaining hands to navigate the vessels.

Formerly when the government wished to send any important functionary such as a judge or a military commandant into the interior, they equipped a swift-sailing *galeota*, manned with ten or a dozen Indians. These could travel, on the average, in one day farther than the ordinary sailing craft could in three. Indian paddlers were now, however, almost impossible to be obtained, and government officers were obliged to travel as passengers in trading vessels. The voyage made in this way was tedious in the extreme. When the regular east wind blew—the *vento geral*, or trade wind of the Amazon—sailing vessels could get along very well; but when this failed, they were obliged to remain, sometimes many days together, anchored near the shore, or progress laboriously by means of the *espia*.

The latter mode of traveling was as follows. The montaria, with twenty or thirty fathoms of cable, one end of which was attached to the foremast, was sent ahead with a couple of hands who secured the other end of the rope to some strong bough or tree trunk; the crew then hauled the vessel up to the point, after which the men in the boat reembarked the cable and paddled forward to repeat the process.

In the dry season, from August to December, when the trade wind is strong and the currents slack, a schooner could reach the mouth of the Rio Negro, a thousand miles from Belém, in about forty days; but in the wet season, from January to July, when the east wind no longer blows and the Amazon pours forth its full volume of water, flooding the banks and producing a tearing current, it took three months to travel the same distance. It was a great blessing to the inhabitants when, in 1853, a line of steamers was established, and this same journey could be accomplished with ease and comfort, at all seasons, in eight days!

THE WALLACES' VOYAGE
UP THE AMAZON RIVER

[WALLACE] We now prepared for our voyage up the Amazon, and, from information we obtained of the country, determined first to go as far as Santarém, a town about five hundred miles up the river, and the seat of a considerable trade. We had to wait a long time to procure a passage, but at length with some difficulty agreed to go in a small empty canoe returning to Santarém.

We were to have the hold to ourselves, and found it very redolent of salt-fish, and some hides

which still remained in it did not improve the odor.
But voyagers on the Amazon must not be fastidious,
so we got our things on board and hung up our hammocks as conveniently as we could for the journey.

Our canoe had a very uneven deck, and, we soon
found, a very leaky one, which annoyed us much by
wetting our clothes and hammocks; and there were
no bulwarks, which, in the quiet waters of the Amazon, are not necessary. We laid in a good stock of
provisions for the voyage, and borrowed some books
from our English and American friends to help to
pass away the time; and in the beginning of August,
left Belém with a fine wind which soon carried us beyond the islands opposite the city into the wide river
beyond. The next day we crossed the little sea formed
opposite the mouth of the Tocantins, and sailed up a
fine stream till we entered again among islands, and
soon got into the narrow channel which forms the
communication between the Pará and Amazon rivers. . . .

We proceeded for several days in those narrow
channels, which form a network of water—a labyrinth quite unknown except to the inhabitants of the
district. We had to wait daily for the tide, and then
to help ourselves on by warping along shore, there
being no wind. A small montaria was sent on ahead
with a long rope, which the Indians fastened to some
projecting tree or bush, and then returned with the
other end to the large canoe, which was pulled up by
it. The rope was then taken on again, and the operation repeated continually till the tide turned, when
we could not make way against the current.

In many parts of the channel I was much
pleased with the bright colors of the leaves, which

displayed all the variety of autumnal tints in England. The cause, however, was different: the leaves were here budding instead of falling. On first opening they were pale reddish, then bright red, brown, and lastly green; some were yellow, some ocher, and some copper-colored, which, together with various shades of green, produced a most beautiful appearance.

It was about ten days after we left Belém that the stream began to widen out and the tide to flow into the Amazon instead of into the Pará river, giving us the longer ebb to make way with. In about two days more we were in the Amazon itself, and it was with emotions of admiration and awe that we gazed upon the stream of this mighty and far-famed river. Our imagination wandered to its sources in the distant Andes, to the Peruvian Incas of old, to the silver mountains of Potosi and to the gold-seeking Spaniards and wild Indians who now inhabit the country about its thousand sources. What a grand idea it was to think that we now saw the accumulated waters of a course of three thousand miles, that all the streams that for a length of twelve hundred miles drained from the snow-clad Andes were here congregated in the wide extent of ocher-colored water spread out before us! Venezuela, Colombia, Ecuador, Peru, Bolivia, and Brazil—six mighty states, spreading over a country far larger than Europe—had each contributed to form the flood which bore us so peacefully on its bosom.

We now felt the influence of the easterly wind, which during the whole of the summer months blows pretty steadily up the Amazon and enables vessels to make way against its powerful current. Sometimes we had thunderstorms, with violent squalls which, as they were generally in the right direction, helped us along the faster; and twice we ran aground on shoals, which caused us some trouble and delay. We had partly to unload the canoe into the montaria, and then, by getting out anchors in the deep water, managed after some hard pulling to extricate ourselves. Sometimes we caught fish, which were a great luxury for us, or went on shore to purchase fruit at some Indian's cottage.

The most striking features of the Amazon are its vast expanse of smooth water, generally from three to six miles wide; its pale yellowish-olive color; the great beds of aquatic grass which line its shores, large masses of which are often detached and form floating islands; the quantity of fruits and leaves and great trunks of trees which it carries down: and its level banks clad with lofty unbroken forest. In places the white stems and leaves of the cecropias give a peculiar aspect, and in others the straight dark trunks of lofty forest trees form a living wall along the water's edge.

There is much animation too on this giant stream. Numerous flocks of parrots, and the great red and yellow macaws, fly across every morning and evening, uttering their hoarse cries. Many kinds of herons and rails frequent the marshes on its banks, and the large handsome Orinoco goose (*Neochen jubatus*) is often seen swimming about the bays and inlets.

But perhaps the most characteristic birds of the Amazon are the gulls and terns, which are in great abundance. All night long their cries are heard over the sandbanks, where they deposit their eggs, and during the day they constantly attracted our attention by their habit of sitting in a row on a floating log, sometimes a dozen or twenty side by side, and going for miles down the stream as grave and motionless as if they were on some very important business. These birds deposit their eggs in little hollows in the sand, and the Indians say that during the heat of the day they carry water in their beaks to moisten them and prevent their being roasted by the glowing rays of the sun. Besides these there are divers and darters in abundance, porpoises are constantly blowing in every direction, and alligators are often seen slowly swimming across the river.

On the north bank of the Amazon, for about two hundred miles, are ranges of low hills which, as well as the country between them, are partly bare and partly covered with brush and thickets. They vary from three hundred to one thousand feet high, and extend inland, being probably connected with the mountains of Cayenne and Guiana. After passing them there are no more hills visible from the river for more than two thousand miles till we reach the lowest ranges of the Andes: they are called the Serras de Paru, and terminate in the Serras de Monte Alegre, near the little village of Monte Alegre, about one hundred miles below Santarém.

A few other small villages were passed, and here and there some Brazilian's country house or Indian's cottage, often completely buried in the forest. Fishermen were sometimes seen in their canoes, and now and then a large schooner passing down the middle of the river, while often for a whole day we would not pass a house or see a human being. The wind, too, was seldom enough for us to make way against the stream, and then we had to proceed by the laborious and tedious method of warping already described.

At length, after a prolonged voyage of twenty-eight days, we reached Santarém at the mouth of the river Tapajoz, whose blue, transparent waters formed a most pleasing contrast to the turbid stream of the Amazon.

It was now November, and as some rain had fallen and gloomy weather had set in, we determined to start for the Rio Negro as soon as we could. Our canoe was at length ready, having taken us a long time to repair the bottom, which was quite rotten.

We went along slowly, now and then sailing but generally rowing, and suffering much annoyance from the rain, which was almost incessant. The mosquitoes too were a great torture. Night after night we were kept in a state of feverish irritation, unable to close our eyes for a moment. . . .

Toward the end of December we reached the little village of Itacoatiara, where we found a *festa*, or procession, going on—a number of women and girls, with ribands and flowers, dancing along to the church with the priest at their head, in a most ludicrous manner. In the evening we went to the house where the dancing took place and had some wine and sweetmeats. We bought here some coffee and a large basket of plantains.

On Christmas Day we reached a house where they had just caught a quantity of fish, and we wanted to buy some, which was refused; but they gave us a fine fat piece for our dinner. We bought some eggs, and when we stopped for the day, concocted a farina pudding, and so, with our fish and coffee, made a very tolerable Christmas dinner, while eating which our thoughts turned to our distant home and to dear friends who at their more luxurious tables would think of us far away upon the Amazon.

On the 31st of December, 1849, we arrived at the city of Manaus on the Rio Negro. On the evening of the thirtieth the sun had set on the yellow Amazon, but we continued rowing till late at night, when we reached some rocks at the mouth of the Rio Negro, and caught some fine fish in the shallows. In the morning we looked with surprise at the wonderful change in the water around us. We might have fancied ourselves on the river Styx, for it was black as ink in every direction, except where the white sand, seen at the depth of a few feet through its dusky wave, appeared of a golden hue. The water itself is of a pale-brown color, the tinge being just perceptible in a glass, while in deep water it appears jet black, and well deserves its name of Rio Negro, "black river."

The great feature of [the Rio Negro] is its enormous width, often fifteen or twenty miles, and its being so crowded with islands, all densely forest clad and often of great extent, that for a distance of nearly five hundred miles it is only at rare intervals that the northern bank is visible from the southern, or vice versa. For the first four hundred and fifty miles of its course the country is a great forest plain, the banks mostly of alluvial clays and sands, though there are occasional patches of sandstone. Then commences the great granitic plateau of the upper river, with isolated mountains and rock pillars, extending over the watershed to the cataracts of the Orinoco, to the mountains of Guiana, and perhaps in some parts up to the foot of the Andes. The other great peculiarity of the river is its dark-brown or nearly black waters which are yet perfectly clear and pleasant to drink. This is due no doubt to the greater part of the river's basin being an enormous forest-covered plain, and its chief tributaries flowing over granite rocks. . . . A delightful peculiarity of all these black, or clear water, rivers is that their shores are entirely free from mosquitoes. . . .

[The Uaupés River flows] through a densely wooded country, with nowhere more than a few hundred yards of clear ground on its banks, with a very crooked and twisted course, and with a current varying from being scarcely perceptible to such rapidity that a whole crew of paddlers can hardly make way against it. . . .

[It is] a river perhaps unsurpassed for the difficulties and dangers of its navigation. We had passed fifty *cachoeiras*, great and small; some were mere rapids, others furious cataracts, and some nearly perpendicular falls. About twenty were rapids, up which, by the help of a long cipó attached to the canoe instead of a rope, we were pulled without much difficulty. About eighteen were very bad and dangerous, requiring the canoe to be partially unloaded where practicable, and all the exertions of my Indians, often with additional assistance, to pass; and twelve were so high and furious as to require the canoe to be entirely unloaded and either pulled over the dry and often very precipitous rocks or, with almost equal difficulty, up the margin of the fall.

During the two ascents and descents of the Rio Negro and Uaupés in 1850–1852 I took observations with a prismatic compass, not only of the course of the canoe, but also of every visible point, hill, house, or channel between the islands, so as to be able to map this little-known river. For the distances I timed our journey by a good watch, and estimated the rate of travel up or down the river, and whether paddling or sailing.

With my sextant I determined several latitudes by altitudes of the sun or of some of the fixed stars. The longitudes of Manaus and of San Carlos, near the mouth of the Casiquiare, had been determined by previous travelers, and my aim was to give a tolerable idea of the course and width of the river between these points, and to map the almost unknown river Uaupés for the first four hundred miles of its course.

Canoes of different sizes do not travel at very different rates when each has its complement of men, and I had taken many opportunities to ascertain this rate in still water. Then by noting the time occupied for a particular distance, say between two of the cataracts, both during the ascent and descent of the river, the mean of the two would be the time if there were no current. Making a little allowance for the load in the canoe, the number or the quality of the rowers, etc., this time multiplied by the rate of travel in still water would give the distance. This was the plan I adopted in making my map of the Uaupés.

BATES'S FIRST TRIP TO
THE UPPER AMAZON

[BATES] I embarked at Manaus on the 26th of March, 1850, three years before steamers were introduced on the upper river, in a *cuberta* which was returning to Tefé, the first and only town of any importance in the vast solitude of the Solimões, from

Santarém, whither it had been sent with a cargo of turtle oil in earthenware jars. The owner, an old white-haired Portuguese trader of Tefé named Daniel Cardozo, was then at Manaus. . . . He was about to leave Manaus himself in a small boat, and recommended me to send forward my heavy baggage in the cuberta and make the journey with him. He would reach Tefé, three hundred and seventy miles distant from Manaus, in twelve or fourteen days; whilst the large vessel would be thirty or forty days on the road. I preferred, however, to go in company with my luggage, looking forward to the many opportunities I should have of landing and making collections on the banks of the river.

I shipped the collections made between Belém and the Rio Negro in a large cutter which was about descending to the capital, and after a heavy day's work got all my chests aboard the Tefé canoe by eight o'clock at night. The Indians were then all embarked, one of them being brought dead drunk by his companions and laid to sober himself all night on the wet boards of the *tombadilho* [quarter-deck]. The cabo, a spirited young white named Estulano Alves Carneiro, who has since risen to be a distinguished citizen of the new province of the Upper Amazon, soon after gave orders to get up the anchor. The men took to the oars, and in a few hours we crossed the broad mouth of the Rio Negro, the night being clear, calm, and starlit, and the surface of the inky waters smooth as a lake.

When I awoke the next morning, we were progressing by espia along the left bank of the Solimões. The rainy season had now set in over the region through which the great river flows; the sandbanks and all the lower lands were already under water, and the tearing current, two or three miles in breadth, bore along a continuous line of uprooted trees and islets of floating plants.

The prospect was most melancholy: no sound was heard but the dull murmur of the waters; the coast along which we traveled all day was encumbered every step of the way with fallen trees, some of which quivered in the currents which set around projecting points of land. Our old pest, the motuca [a large and troublesome fly], began to torment us as soon as the sun gained power in the morning. White egrets were plentiful at the edge of the water, and hummingbirds, in some places, were whirring about the flowers overhead. The desolate appearance of the landscape increased after sunset, when the moon rose in mist.

This upper river, the Alto-Amazonas, or Solimões, is always spoken of by the Brazilians as a distinct stream. This is partly owing . . . to the direction it seems to take at the fork of the Rio Negro; the inhabitants of the country, from their partial knowledge, not being able to comprehend the whole river system in one view. It has, however, many peculiarities to distinguish it from the lower course of the river.

The trade wind, or sea breeze, which reaches, in the height of the dry season, as far as the mouth of the Rio Negro, nine hundred or a thousand miles from the Atlantic, never blows on the upper river. The atmosphere is therefore more stagnant and sultry, and the winds that do prevail are of irregular direction and short duration.

A great part of the land on the borders of the Lower Amazon is hilly; there are extensive *campos*, or open plains, and long stretches of sandy soil clothed with thinner forests. The climate, in consequence, is

comparatively dry, many months in succession during
the fine season passing without rain.

All this is changed on the Solimões. A fortnight
of clear sunny weather is a rarity: the whole region
through which the river and its affluents flow, after
leaving the easternmost ridges of the Andes . . .
240 miles from the Pacific, is a vast plain, about 1000
miles in length and 500 or 600 in breadth, covered
with one uniform, lofty, impervious, and humid forest. The soil is nowhere sandy, but always either a'
stiff clay, alluvium, or vegetable mold, which latter, in
many places, is seen in water-worn sections of the
river banks to be twenty or thirty feet in depth.

With such a soil and climate, the luxuriance of
vegetation and the abundance and beauty of animal
forms, which are already so great in the region nearer
the Atlantic, increase on the upper river. The fruits,
both wild and cultivated, common to the two sections of the country, reach a progressively larger size
in advancing westward, and some trees which blossom only once a year at Belém and Santarém yield
flower and fruit all the year round at Tefé. The climate is healthy, although one lives here as in a permanent vapor bath. . . .

I resided and traveled on the Solimões altogether for four years and a half. The country on its
borders is a magnificent wilderness where civilized
man as yet has scarcely obtained a footing; the cultivated ground from the Rio Negro to the Andes
amounting only to a few score acres. Man, indeed, in
any condition, from his small numbers, makes but an
insignificant figure in these vast solitudes.

It may be mentioned that the Solimões is 2130
miles in length if we reckon from the source of what
is usually considered the main stream (Lake Lauri-

cocha near Lima), but 2500 miles by the route of the Ucayali, the most considerable and practicable fork of the upper part of the river. It is navigable at all seasons by large steamers for upward of 1400 miles from the mouth of the Rio Negro. . . .

After the first two or three days we fell into a regular way of life aboard. . . . We landed twice a day to give ourselves and the Indians a little rest and change and to cook our two meals—breakfast and dinner. . . . At every landing place I had a ramble in the forest whilst the redskins made the fire and cooked the meal. The result was a large daily addition to my collection of insects, reptiles, and shells. Sometimes the neighborhood of our gypsylike encampment was a tract of dry and spacious forest, pleasant to ramble in; but more frequently it was a rank wilderness into which it was impossible to penetrate many yards on account of uprooted trees, entangled webs of monstrous woody climbers, thickets of spiny bamboos, swamps, or obstacles of one kind or another.

Canoemen on the Upper Amazon live in constant dread of the *terra caídas,* or landslips, which occasionally take place along the steep earthy banks, especially when the waters are rising. Large vessels are sometimes overwhelmed by these avalanches of earth and trees. I should have thought the accounts of them exaggerated if I had not had an opportunity during this voyage of seeing one on a large scale.

One morning I was awoke before sunrise by an unusual sound resembling the roar of artillery. I was lying alone on the top of the cabin; it was very dark and all my companions were asleep, so I lay listening. The sounds came from a considerable distance, and the crash which had aroused me was succeeded by others much less formidable. The first explanation which occurred to me was that it was an earthquake, for although the night was breathlessly calm, the broad river was much agitated and the vessel rolled heavily.

Soon after, another loud explosion took place, apparently much nearer than the former one; then followed others. The thundering peal rolled backward and forward now seeming close at hand, now far off, the sudden crashes being often succeeded by a pause or a long-continued dull rumbling. At the second explosion, Vicente, who lay snoring by the helm, awoke and told me it was a terra caída, but I could scarcely believe him.

The day dawned after the uproar had lasted about an hour, and we then saw the work of destruction going forward on the other side of the river, about three miles off. Large masses of forest, including trees of colossal size, probably two hundred feet in height, were rocking to and fro, and falling headlong one after the other into the water. After each avalanche the wave which it caused returned on the crumbly bank with tremendous force, and caused the fall of other masses by undermining them.

The line of coast over which the landslip extended was a mile or two in length; the end of it, however, was hid from our view by an intervening island. It was a grand sight; each downfall created a cloud of spray; the concussion in one place causing other masses to give way a long distance from it, and thus the crashes continued, swaying to and fro, with little prospect of termination. When we glided out of sight two hours after sunrise, the destruction was still going on.

3

GRASSY PLAINS
AND
FLOODED FORESTS

... the soil, vegetation and animal tenants ... are widely different. ...
    BATES, *Naturalist on the Amazons*

■ Santarém, at the midpoint on the Lower Amazon,
was Bates's headquarters for three and a half years. It
stands at the mouth of the Tapajoz River, another of
the major tributaries of the Amazon from the south,
in an area that is in striking contrast to the region
around Belém and also to the forests of the Upper
Amazon.

Santarém itself was a delightful place, an attrac-
tive town with an agreeable climate. Here the dry
season was really dry, not just a lesser amount of rain
as at Belém or farther up the river, and the grassland
or campo vegetation reflected the difference.

The grasslands of the world (prairie, steppe,
pampas, and savanna or campos) occur in both tem-

perate and tropical regions where there are distinct wet and dry seasons. Rainfall in these areas is generally not adequate for forests, but even trees that might grow are usually discouraged by other determinants of such regions, grazing animals or frequent fires. (Although men often set fires to burn off dried grass, they are also caused by lightning.) Still, there may be scattered trees, particularly along water courses.

As Bates observed, the life habits of the plants and animals mirrored these seasonal changes.

Bates would have liked to explore the campos, but "complete solitude reigns over the whole stretch of this beautiful country. The inhabitants of Santarém know nothing of the interior and seem to feel little curiosity concerning it. A few tracks from the town across the campo lead to some small clearings four or five miles off . . . but excepting these, there are no roads or signs of the proximity of a civilized settlement." Consequently his explorations were mostly confined to the river edges.

The river edges, however, are also unique, "for a great extent of land on the banks of all the rivers is flooded to a great depth at every time of high water. These lands are called, in the language of the country, *igapó,* and are one of the most singular features of the Amazon. Sometimes on one side, sometimes on both, to a distance of twenty or thirty miles from the main river, these igapós extend on the Amazon, and on portions of all its great branches. They are all covered with a dense virgin forest of lofty trees whose stems are, every year, during six months, from ten to forty feet under water."

As in the campos, there are plants, animals, and even Indian tribes adapted to these strange conditions, and Wallace investigated them with his usual zest. One of his special prizes here was the umbrella bird, a member of the peculiar cotinga family. His description of this rare find marked his entry into print and was the first of literally hundreds of scientific and popular papers and books that he wrote over the next sixty-odd years.

SANTARÉM

[BATES] Santarém . . . is the most civilized and important settlement on the banks of the main river from Peru to the Atlantic. The pretty little town, or city, as it is called, with its rows of tolerably uniform whitewashed and red-tiled houses surrounded by green gardens and woods, stands on gently sloping ground on the eastern side of the Tapajoz close to its point of junction with the Amazon. A small eminence on which a fort has been erected, but which is now in a dilapidated condition, overlooks the streets and forms the eastern limit of the mouth of the tributary.

The Tapajoz at Santarém is contracted to a breadth of about a mile and a half by an accretion of low alluvial land which forms a kind of delta on the western side; fifteen miles farther up the river is seen at its full width of ten or a dozen miles, and the magnificent hilly country through which it flows from the south is then visible on both shores. This high land, which appears to be a continuation of the central tablelands of Brazil, stretches almost without interruption on the eastern side of the river down to its mouth at Santarém.

The scenery as well as the soil, vegetation, and

animal tenants of this region are widely different from those of the flat and uniform country which borders the Amazon along most part of its course. After traveling week after week on the main river, the aspect of Santarém, with its broad white sandy beach, limpid dark-green waters, and line of picturesque hills rising behind the fringe of green forest, affords an agreeable surprise. On the main Amazon the prospect is monotonous unless the vessel runs near the shore, when the wonderful diversity and beauty of the vegetation afford constant entertainment. Otherwise the unvaried, broad yellow stream and the long, low line of forest, which dwindles away in a broken line of trees on the sealike horizon and is renewed, reach after reach, as the voyager advances, weary by their uniformity.

I arrived at Santarém on my second journey into the interior in November 1851, and made it my headquarters for a period, as it turned out, of three years and a half. During this time I made, in pursuance of the plan I had framed, many excursions up the Tapajoz, and to other places of interest in the surrounding region.

On landing I found no difficulty in hiring a suitable house on the outskirts of the place. It was pleasantly situated near the beach, going toward the *aldeia* or Indian part of the town. The ground sloped from the back premises down to the waterside, and my little raised veranda overlooked a beautiful flower garden, a great rarity in this country, which belonged to the neighbors. The house contained only three rooms, one with brick and two with boarded floors. It was substantially built, like all the better sort of houses in Santarém, and had a stuccoed front. The kitchen, as is usual, formed an outhouse placed a few yards distant from the other rooms. . . .

In engaging servants I had the good fortune to meet with a free mulatto, an industrious and trustworthy young fellow named José, willing to arrange with me; the people of his family cooking for us whilst he assisted me in collecting; he proved of the greatest service in the different excursions we subsequently made. Servants of any kind were almost impossible to be obtained at Santarém, free people being too proud to hire themselves and slaves too few and valuable to their masters to be let out to others. These matters arranged, the house put in order, and a rude table, with a few chairs, bought or borrowed to furnish the house with, I was ready in three or four days to commence my natural history explorations in the neighborhood. . . .

Santarém is a pleasant place to live in. . . . There are no insect pests, mosquito, pium, sandfly, or motuca. The climate is glorious: during six months of the year, from August to February, very little rain falls and the sky is cloudless for weeks together, the fresh breezes from the sea, nearly four hundred miles distant, moderating the great heat of the sun. . . . The streets are always clean and dry, even in the height of the wet season, good order is always kept, and the place pretty well supplied with provisions. None but those who have suffered from the difficulty of obtaining the necessaries of life at any price in most of the interior settlements of South America can appreciate the advantages of Santarém in this respect.

The country around Santarém is not clothed with dense and lofty forest like the rest of the great humid river plain of the Amazon. It is a campo region, a slightly elevated and undulating tract of land, wooded only in patches or with single scattered trees. . . . The surface is carpeted with slender hairy grasses, unfit for pasture, growing to a uniform height of about a foot. The patches of wood look like copses in the middle of green meadows. . . . They are composed of a great variety of trees, loaded with succulent parasites and lashed together by woody climbers like the forest in other parts. . . .

The appearance of the campos changes very much according to the season. There is not that grand uniformity of aspect throughout the year which is observed in the virgin forest and which makes a deeper impression on the naturalist the longer he remains in this country. The seasons in this part of the Amazon region are sharply contrasted, but the difference is not so great as in some tropical countries, where, during the dry monsoon, insects and reptiles go into a summer sleep and the trees simultaneously shed their leaves.

As the dry season advances (August, September), the grass on the campos withers and the shrubby vegetation near the town becomes a mass of parched yellow stubble. The period, however, is not one of general torpidity or repose for animal or vegetable life. Birds certainly are not so numerous as in the wet season, but some kinds remain and lay their eggs at this time—for instance, the ground doves (*Columbina*). The trees retain their verdure throughout and many of them flower in the dry months. Lizards do not become torpid, and insects are seen both in the larva and the perfect states, showing that the aridity of the climate has not a gen-

eral influence on the development of the species.
Some kinds of butterflies, especially the little hair-
streaks (*Thecla*) whose caterpillars feed on the trees,
make their appearance only when the dry season is at
its height. The land mollusks of the district are the
only animals which aestivate; they are found in clusters, *Bulimus* and *Helix*, concealed in hollow trees,
the mouths of their shells closed by a film of mucus.

The fine weather breaks up often with great sud-
denness about the beginning of February. Violent
squalls from the west, or the opposite direction to the
trade wind, then occur. . . . They are accompanied
with terrific electric explosions, the sharp claps of
thunder falling almost simultaneously with the blind-
ing flashes of lightning. . . . After a week or two of
showery weather the aspect of the country is completely changed. The parched ground in the neighborhood of Santarém breaks out, so to speak, in a
rash of greenery: the dusty, languishing trees gain,
without having shed their old leaves, a new clothing
of tender green foliage; a wonderful variety of quick-
growing leguminous plants springs up, and leafy
creepers overrun the ground, the bushes, and the
trunks of trees.

One is reminded of the sudden advent of spring
after a few warm showers in northern climates; I was
the more struck by it as nothing similar is witnessed
in the virgin forests amongst which I had passed the
four years previous to my stay in this part. The grass
on the campos is renewed, and many of the campo
trees, especially the myrtles, which grow abundantly
in one portion of the district, begin to flower, attract-
ing by the fragrance of their blossoms a great number
and variety of insects, more particularly Coleoptera.

Many kinds of birds: parrots, toucans, and barbets, which live habitually in the forest, then visit the open places. A few weeks of comparatively dry weather generally intervene in March, after a month or two of rain. The heaviest rains fall in April, May, and June; they come in a succession of showers, with sunny gleamy weather in the intervals.

June and July are the months when the leafy luxuriance of the campos and the activity of life are at their highest. Most birds have then completed their molting, which extends over the period from February to May. The flowering shrubs are then mostly in bloom, and numberless kinds of dipterous and hymenopterous insects appear simultaneously with the flowers. This season might be considered the equivalent of summer in temperate climates, as the bursting forth of the foliage in February represents the spring. But under the equator there is not that simultaneous march in the annual life of animals and plants which we see in high latitudes, some species, it is true, are dependent upon others in their periodical acts of life and go hand in hand with them, but they are not all simultaneously and similarly affected by the physical changes of the seasons.

THE IGAPÓ

[WALLACE] . . . nothing could make up for the desolation and death which the incessant rains appeared to have produced in all animate nature. Between two and three months passed away in this unexciting monotony when, the river having nearly risen to its height and there being some appearance of the weather improving, I determined on taking a journey to the Solimões (as the Amazon is called above the entrance of the Rio Negro), to the estate of . . . my kind host's father-in-law.

The river was now so high that a great portion of the lowlands between the Rio Negro and the Amazon was flooded, being what is called igapó. This is one of the most singular features of the Amazon. It extends from a little above Santarém up to the confines of Peru—a distance of about seventeen hundred miles—and varies in width on each side of the river from one to ten or twenty miles.

From Santarém to Coari, a little town on the Solimões, a person may go by canoe in the wet season without once entering into the main river. He will pass through small streams, lakes, and swamps, and everywhere around him will stretch out an illimitable waste of waters, but all covered with lofty virgin forest. For days he will travel through this forest, scraping against tree trunks and stooping to pass beneath the leaves of prickly palms now level with the water, though raised on stems forty feet high. In this trackless maze the Indian finds his way with unerring certainty, and by slight indications of broken twigs or scraped bark, goes on day by day as if traveling on a beaten road.

In the igapó peculiar animals are found, attracted by the fruits of trees which grow only there. In fact the Indians assert that every tree that grows in the igapó is distinct from all those found in other districts; and when we consider the extraordinary conditions under which these plants exist, being submerged for six months of the year till they are sufficiently lofty to rise above the highest water level, it does not seem improbable that such may be the case.

Many species of trogons are peculiar to the igapó, others to the dry virgin forest. The umbrella bird is entirely confined to it, as is also the little bristle-tailed manakin. Some monkeys are found there only in the wet season, and whole tribes of Indians, such as the Purupurus and Muras, entirely inhabit it, building small, easily removable huts on the sandy shores in the dry season, and on rafts in the wet, spending a great part of their lives in canoes, sleeping suspended in rude hammocks from trees over the deep water, cultivating no vegetables, but subsisting entirely on the fish, turtle, and cowfish [manatee] which they obtain from the river.

On crossing the Rio Negro from the city of Manaus, we entered into a tract of this description. Our canoe was forced under branches and among dense bushes till we got into a part where the trees were loftier and a deep gloom prevailed. Here the lowest branches of the trees were level with the surface of the water and were many of them putting forth flowers. As we proceeded we sometimes came to a grove of small palms, the leaves being now only a few feet above us, and among them was the *marajá*, bearing bunches of agreeable fruit which, as we passed, the Indians cut off with their long knives. Sometimes the rustling of leaves overhead told us that monkeys were near, and we would soon perhaps discover them peeping down from among the thick foliage and then bounding rapidly away as soon as we had caught a glimpse of them.

Presently we came out into the sunshine in a grassy lake filled with lilies and beautiful water plants, little yellow bladderworts (*Utricularia*), and the bright blue flowers and curious leaves with swollen stalks of the pontederias.

Again in the gloom of the forest, among the lofty cylindrical trunks rising like columns out of the deep water: now a splashing of falling fruit around us would announce that birds were feeding overhead and we could discover a flock of parakeets, or some bright blue cotingas, or the lovely pompadour, with its delicate white wings and claret-colored plumage; now with a whirr a trogon would seize a fruit on the wing, or some clumsy toucan make the branches shake as he alighted.

But what lovely yellow flower is that suspended in the air between two trunks, yet far from either? It shines in the gloom as if its petals were of gold. Now we pass close by it and see its stalk, like a slender wire a yard and a half long, springing from a cluster of thick leaves on the bark of a tree. It is an *Oncidium*, one of the lovely orchis tribe, making these gloomy shades gay with its airy and brilliant flowers. Presently there are more of them, and then others appear, with white and spotted and purple blossoms, some growing on rotten logs floating in the water, but most on moss and decaying bark just above it. There is one magnificent species four inches across, called by the natives St. Ann's flower (flor de Santa Anna), of a brilliant purple color and emitting a most delightful odor; it is a new species and the most magnificent flower of its kind in these regions. Even the natives will sometimes deign to admire it and to wonder how such a beautiful flower grows *à toa* (uselessly) in the igapó.

THE UMBRELLA BIRD

The next morning my hunter arrived, and immediately went out in his canoe among the islands, where the umbrella birds are found. In the evening after dark he returned, bringing one fine specimen. This singular bird . . . inhabits the flooded islands of the Rio Negro and the Solimões, never appearing on the mainland. It feeds on fruits and utters a loud, hoarse cry like some deep musical instrument; whence its Indian name, *ueramimbé*, trumpet bird.

The whole of the neck, where the plume of feathers springs from, is covered internally with a thick coat of hard, muscular fat, very difficult to be cleaned away—which, in preparing the skins, must be done, as it would putrefy and cause the feathers to drop off.

The birds are tolerably abundant, but are shy and perch on the highest trees, and being very muscular, will not fall unless severely wounded. My hunter worked very perseveringly to get them, going out before daylight and often not returning till nine or ten at night, yet he never brought me more than two at a time, generally only one, and sometimes none.

I had sent home in 1850 a short paper on the umbrella bird, then almost unknown to British ornithologists. . . . The bird is in size and general appearance like a short-legged crow, being black with metallic-blue tints on the outer margins of the feathers. Its special peculiarity is its wonderful crest. This is formed of a quantity of slender straight feathers which grow on the contractile skin of the top of the head. The shafts of these feathers are white, with a tufted plume at the end, which is glossy blue and almost hairlike. When the bird is flying or feeding, the crest is laid back, forming a compact white mass sloping a little upward, with the terminal plumes forming a tuft behind; but when at rest, the bird expands the crest, which then forms an elongated dome of a fine glossy, deep blue color, extending beyond the beak, and thus completely masking the head. This dome is about five inches long by four or four and a half inches wide.

Another almost equally remarkable feature is a long cylindrical plume of feathers depending from the lower part of the neck. These feathers grow on a fleshy tube as thick as a goose quill and about an inch and a half long. They are large and overlap each other, with margins of a fine metallic blue. The whole skin of the neck is very loose and extensible, and when the crest is expanded the neck is inflated and the cylindrical neck ornament hangs down in front of it.

The effect of these two strange appendages when the bird is at rest and the head turned backward must be to form an irregular ovate black mass with neither legs, head, nor eyes visible, so as to be quite unlike any living thing. It may thus be a protection against arboreal carnivores, owls, etc.

It is undoubtedly one of the most extraordinary of birds, and is an extreme from the great family of cotingas, which are peculiar to tropical America. Strange to say, it is rather nearly allied to the curious white bellbird, so different in color but also possessing a fleshly erectile appendage from the base of the upper mandible. The umbrella bird inhabits the lofty

forests of the islands of the lower Rio Negro and
some portions of the flooded forests of the Upper
Amazon.

A WATER PATH
ON THE UPPER AMAZON

[BATES] The creek is more than a quarter of a mile
broad near the town [of Tefé], but a few miles inland it gradually contracts until it becomes a mere
rivulet flowing through a broad dell in the forest.
When the river rises it fills this dell. The trunks of
the lofty trees then stand many feet deep in the water
and small canoes are able to travel the distance of a
day's journey under the shade, regular paths or alleys
being cut through the branches and lower trees. This
is the general character of the Upper Amazon, a land
of small elevation and abruptly undulated, the hollows forming narrow valleys in the dry months and
deep navigable creeks in the wet months. In retired
nooks on the margins of these shady rivulets a few
families or small hordes of aborigines still linger in
nearly their primitive state, the relics of their once
numerous tribes. . . .

We set out at sunrise, in a small igarité manned
by six young Indian paddlers. After traveling about
three miles along the broad portion of the creek—
which, being surrounded by woods, had the appearance of a large pool—we came to a part where our
course seemed to be stopped by an impenetrable
hedge of trees and bushes. We were some time before
finding the entrance, but when fairly within the
shades a remarkable scene presented itself. . . .

A narrow and tolerably straight alley stretched

away for a long distance before us. On each side were the tops of bushes and young trees, forming a kind of border to the path, and the trunks of the tall forest trees rose at irregular intervals from the water, their crowns interlocking far over our heads and forming a thick shade. Slender air roots hung down in clusters and looping cipós dangled from the lower branches; bunches of grass, tillandsias, and ferns sat in the forks of the larger boughs, and the trunks of trees near the water had adhering to them round dried masses of freshwater sponges. There was no current perceptible, and the water was stained of a dark olive-brown hue, but the submerged stems could be seen through it to a great depth.

We traveled at good speed for three hours along this shady road. . . . When the paddlers rested for a time, the stillness and gloom of the place became almost painful: our voices waked dull echoes as we conversed, and the noise made by fishes occasionally whipping the surface of the water was quite startling. A cool, moist, clammy air pervaded the sunless shade.

The breadth of the wooded valley at the commencement is probably more than half a mile and there is a tolerably clear view for a considerable distance on each side of the water path through the irregular colonnade of trees: other paths also, in this part, branch off right and left from the principal road, leading to the scattered houses of Indians on the mainland.

The dell contracts gradually toward the head of the rivulet, and the forest then becomes denser; the water path also diminishes in width and becomes more winding on account of the closer growth of the trees. The boughs of some are stretched forth at no great height over one's head and are seen to be loaded with epiphytes; one orchid I noticed particularly, on account of its bright yellow flowers growing at the end of flower stems several feet long. Some of the trunks, especially those of palms, close beneath their crowns, were clothed with a thick mass of glossy, shield-shaped *Pothos* plants, mingled with ferns.

Arrived at this part we were in fact in the heart of the virgin forest. We heard no noises of animals in the trees and saw only one bird, the purple-breasted cotinga, sitting alone on a high branch. For some distance the lower vegetation was so dense that the road runs under an arcade of foliage, the branches having been cut away only sufficiently to admit of the passage of a small canoe.

These thickets are formed chiefly of bamboos, whose slender foliage and curving stems arrange themselves in elegant, feathery bowers: but other social plants—slender green climbers with tendrils so eager in aspiring to grasp the higher boughs that they seem to be endowed almost with animal energy—and certain low trees having large, elegantly veined leaves, contribute also to the jungly masses. Occasionally we came upon an uprooted tree lying across the path, its voluminous crown still held up by thick cables of cipó connecting it with standing trees: a wide circuit had to be made in these cases, and it was sometimes difficult to find the right path again.

At length we arrived at our journey's end. We were then in a very dense and gloomy part of the forest. We could see, however, the dry land on both sides of the creek, and to our right a small sunny opening appeared, the landing place to the native dwellings.

4

JAGUARS
AND INDIANS

Every day showed us something fresh to
admire, some new wonder. . . .
WALLACE, *Travels on the Amazon*

■ Wallace's first trip up the Rio Negro took him north
beyond its headwaters into Venezuela. On the way he
passed a historic spot, San Carlos, "the principal Ven-
ezuelan village on the Rio Negro . . . the farthest
point reached by Humboldt from an opposite direction. . . . I was therefore now entering upon ground
gone over fifty years before by that illustrious traveler."

Shortly afterward he passed the entrance to the
Casiquiare, a river that rises in the mountainous area
to the east and then divides into two streams, one
feeding the Rio Negro and the other the Orinoco
River. Some miles beyond this point he turned up a
small river and landed at a tiny village consisting of

two houses. "From this place a road leads overland about ten miles through the forest to Javita, a village on the Temi, a branch of the Atabapo, which flows into the Orinoco." He had "thus crossed the division between the basins of the Amazon and the Orinoco" and had reached his destination in this direction.

The road itself, then a portage between the two great river systems, was one of the greatest rarities in the tropical forest, and Wallace remained at Javita for more than a month to take advantage of this unusual opportunity for collecting. In spite of poor weather he was able to add many new and different species of animals, particularly insects, besides a number of fishes from the nearby streams.

On an exploratory trip of the River Uaupés, an almost unknown tributary of the Rio Negro, Wallace had met his first "true, wild Indians." Returning for a second and longer ascent of this dangerous river, he collected information and artifacts of thirty different tribes. He was greatly impressed by the dignity and harmony of the lives of these Indians, still undisturbed by the conflicting values of the European white man.

Bates, on the other hand, found the Indians impassive and unimaginative, and he thought them uninteresting companions. Perhaps as a result, he made no effort to study the different tribes and their customs. As "unoffending strangers," however, neither he nor Wallace ever had any real trouble with the Indians other than difficulties in hiring them.

But the Indians were never numerous (and sad to say, they have been ruthlessly exterminated even up to the present time). In fact, Bates did not find them as well adapted to the tropical climate as the imported Negroes or as he. He often noticed that they suffered even more from the heat than he did. As comparatively recent immigrants into the tropical lowlands, the Indians' adjustment to the climate apparently still left something to be desired.

Wallace rarely stayed for long at any one place, but Bates planned his travels more methodically and spent considerable time on various sections of the river. Tefé, on the Upper Amazon, was his headquarters for four and half years, and he came to know this remote region rather well. In many ways it was distinctly different from other parts of the river, even in the seasons. But in spite of the endless fascinations of the natural scene, both Bates and Wallace suffered from loneliness and missed the association with fellow Europeans.

THE ROAD TO JAVITA

[WALLACE] . . . The following morning we had nothing for breakfast, so I sent the Indians off early to fish, with positive instructions to return by ten o'clock in order that we might get to Javita before night. They chose, however, to stay till past noon, and then came with two or three small fish which did not give us a mouthful apiece. It was thus two o'clock before we started.

I was pretty well loaded with gun, ammunition, insect boxes, etc., but soon got on ahead, with one Indian boy who could not understand a single word of Portuguese. . . .

We still had some miles to go. The sun had set, so we pushed on quickly, my attendant keeping close at my heels. In the marshes and over the little streams we had now some difficulty in finding our way along the narrow trunks laid for bridges. I was barefoot, and every minute stepped on some projecting root or stone or trod sideways upon something which almost dislocated my ankle.

It was now pitch-dark: dull clouds could just be distinguished through the openings in the high arch of overhanging trees, but the road we were walking on was totally invisible. Jaguars, I knew, abounded here, deadly serpents were plentiful, and at every step I almost expected to feel a cold; gliding body under my feet or deadly fangs in my leg. Through the darkness I gazed, expecting momentarily to encounter the glaring eyes of a jaguar or to hear his low growl in the thicket. But to turn back or to stop were alike useless. . . .

At length we came to the clearing I had reached two days before, and I knew that we had but a short distance to go. There were, however, several small streams to cross. Suddenly we would step into water, which we felt but could not see, and then had to find the narrow bridge crossing it. Of the length of the bridge, its height above the water, or the depth of the stream, we were entirely ignorant; and to walk along a trunk four inches wide under such circumstances was rather a nervous matter.

We proceeded, placing one foot before the other and balancing steadily, till we again felt ourselves on firm ground. On one or two occasions I lost my balance, but it was luckily only a foot or two to the ground and water below, though if it had been twenty it would have been all the same. Some half dozen of brooks and bridges like this had to be passed, and several little ups and downs in the road, till at length, emerging from the pitchy shade upon an open space, we saw twinkling lights which told us the village was before us. . . .

I had now reached the farthest point in this direction that I had wished to attain. I had passed the boundary of the mighty Amazon valley and was among the streams that go to swell another of the world's great waters —the Orinoco. A deficiency in all other parts of the Upper Amazon district was here supplied: a road through the virgin forest by which I could readily reach its recesses and where I was more sure of obtaining the curious insects of so distant a region, as well as the birds and other animals which inhabit it. So I determined to remain here at least a month, steadily at work. Every day I went myself along the road, and sent my Indians, some to fish in the little black river Temi, others with their *zarabatanas* [blow-pipes] to seek for the splendid trogons, monkeys, and other curious birds and animals in the forest.

Unfortunately, however, for me, on the very night I reached the village it began to rain, and day after day cloudy and showery weather continued. For three months Javita had enjoyed the most splendid summer weather, with a clear sky and hardly a shower. I had been wasting all this time in the rainy district of the cataracts of the Rio Negro. No one there could tell me that the seasons, at such a short distance, differed so completely, and the consequence was that I arrived at Javita on the very last day of summer.

The winter or rainy season commenced early this year. The river kept rapidly rising. The Indians constantly assured me that it was too soon for the regular rains to commence, that we should have fine weather again, the river would fall, and the winter not set in for two or three weeks. However, such was not the case. Day after day the rain poured down; every afternoon or night was wet, and a little sunshine in the morning was the most we were favored with.

Insects consequently were much more scarce than they otherwise would have been, and the dampness of the atmosphere rendered it extremely difficult to dry and preserve those that I obtained. However, by perseverance I amassed a considerable number of specimens; and what gave me the greatest pleasure was that I almost daily obtained some new species which the Lower Amazon and Rio Negro had not furnished me with. During the time I remained here (forty days), I procured at least forty species of butterflies quite new to me, besides a considerable collection of other orders; and I am sure that during the dry season Javita would be a most productive station for any persevering entomologist. I never saw the great blue butterflies, *Morpho menelaus, M. helenor*, etc., so abundant as here. In certain places in the road I found them by dozens sitting on the ground or on twigs by the roadside, and could easily have captured a dozen or twenty a day if I had wanted them.

In birds and mammalia I did not do much, for my Indians wanted to get back, and were lazy and would not hunt after them. During my walks in the forest I myself saw wild pigs, agoutis, coatis, monkeys, numerous beautiful trogons, and many other fine birds, as well as many kinds of serpents.

One day I had brought me a curious little alligator of a rare species, with numerous ridges and conical tubercles, which I skinned and stuffed, much to the amusement of the Indians, half a dozen of whom gazed intently at the operation.

Of fish, too, I obtained many new species, as my Indians were out fishing every day to provide our supper, and I generally had some to figure and describe in the afternoon. I formed a good collection of the smaller kinds in spirits. My drawings here were made under great difficulties. I generally returned from the forest about three or four in the afternoon, and if I found a new fish, had to set down immediately to figure it before dark. I was thus exposed to the pest of the sandflies, which, every afternoon from four to six, swarm in millions, causing by their bites on the face, ears, and hands the most painful irritation.

Often have I been obliged to start up from my seat, dash down my pencil, and wave my hands about in the cool air to get a little relief. But the sun was getting low and I must return to my task, till, before I had finished, my hands would be as rough and as red as a boiled lobster, and violently inflamed. Bathing them in cold water, however, and half an hour's rest, would bring them to their natural state in which respect the bite of this little insect is far preferable to that of the mosquito, the pium, or the motuca, the effects of whose bites are felt for days.

THE BLACK JAGUAR

As I was walking quietly along, I saw a large jet-black animal come out of the forest about twenty yards before me, which took me so much by surprise that I did not at first imagine what it was. As it moved slowly on and its whole body and long curving tail came into full view in the middle of the road, I saw that it was a fine black jaguar. I involuntarily raised my gun to my shoulder, but remembering that both barrels were loaded with small shot and that to fire would exasperate without killing him, I stood silently gazing. In the middle of the road he turned his head, and for an instant paused and gazed at me, but having, I suppose, other business of his own to attend to, walked steadily on and disappeared in the thicket. As he advanced, I heard the scampering of small animals and the whizzing flight of ground birds clearing the path for their dreaded enemy.

This encounter pleased me much. I was too much surprised, and occupied too much with admiration, to feel fear. I had at length had a full view, in his native wilds, of the rarest variety of the most powerful and dangerous animal inhabiting the American continent. I was, however, by no means desirous of a second meeting, and as it was near sunset, thought it most prudent to turn back toward the village.

"TRUE WILD INDIANS"

The . . . most unexpected sensation of surprise and delight was my first meeting and living with a man in a state of nature—with absolute uncontaminated savages! This was on the Uaupés River, and the surprise of it was that I did not in the least expect to be so surprised. I had already been two years in the country, always among Indians of many tribes; but these were all what are called tame Indians, they wore at least trousers and shirt; they had been (nominally) converted to Christianity, and were under the government of the nearest authorities; and all of them spoke either Portuguese or the common language called *Lingua Geral*.

But these true wild Indians of the Uaupés [who belonged to some thirty different tribes] were at once seen to be something totally different. They had nothing that we call clothes; they had peculiar ornaments, tribal marks, etc.; they all carried weapons or tools of their own manufacture; they are living in a large house, many families together, quite unlike the hut of the tame Indians; but, more than all, their whole aspect and manner were different. They were all going about their own work or pleasure which had nothing to do with white men or their ways; they walked with the free step of the independent forest dweller, and except the few that were known to my companion, paid no attention whatever to us, mere strangers of an alien race.

In every detail they were original and self-sustaining, as are the wild animals of the forests, absolutely independent of civilization, and who could and did live their own lives in their own way, as they had done for countless generations before America was discovered. I could not have believed that there would be so much difference in the aspect of the same people in their native state and when living under European supervision. The true denizen of the Amazonian forests, like the forest itself, is unique and not to be forgotten.

. . . we entered a narrow winding channel, branching from the north bank of the river, and in about an hour reached a *maloca,* or native Indian lodge, the first we had encountered. It was a large, substantial building, near a hundred feet long by about forty wide and thirty high, very strongly constructed of round, smooth, barked timbers and thatched with the fan-shaped leaves of the *caraná* palm. One end was square with a gable, the other circular, and the eaves, hanging over the low walls, reached nearly to the ground. In the middle was a broad aisle formed by the two rows of the principal columns supporting the roof, and between these and the sides were other rows of smaller and shorter timbers; the whole of them were firmly connected by longitudinal and transverse beams at the top, supporting the rafters, and were all bound together with much symmetry by cipós.

Projecting inward from the walls on each side were short partitions of palm thatch exactly similar in arrangement to the boxes in a London eating house or those of a theater. Each of these is the private apartment of a separate family, who thus lives in a sort of patriarchal community. In the side aisles are the farina ovens, *tipitis* for squeezing the mandioca, huge pans and earthen vessels for making *caxiri* [native beer] and other large articles, which appear to be in common; while in every separate apartment are the small pans, stools, baskets, *redes* [hammocks], water pots, weapons, and ornaments of the occupants. The center aisle remains unoccupied and forms a fine walk through the house.

At the circular end is a cross partition or railing about five feet high, cutting off rather more than the semicircle, but with a wide opening in the center. This forms the residence of the chief or head of the maloca, with his wives and children; the more distant relations residing in the other part of the house. The

door at the gable end is very wide and lofty, that at
the circular end is smaller, and these are the only ap-
ertures to admit light and air. The upper part of the
gable is loosely covered with palm leaves hung verti-
cally, through which the smoke of the numerous
wood fires slowly percolates, giving, however, in its
passage a jetty luster to the whole of the upper part of
the roof.

On entering this house I was delighted to find
myself at length in the presence of the true denizens
of the forest. An old and a young man and two
women were the only occupiers, the rest being out on
their various pursuits. The women were absolutely
naked; but on the entrance of the "brancos" they
slipped on a petticoat, with which in these lower parts
of the river they are generally provided but never use
except on such occasions. Their hair was but moderately long, and they were without any ornament but
strongly knitted garters, tightly laced immediately below the knee.

It was the men, however, who presented the
most novel appearance, as different from all the half-
civilized races among whom I had been so long living
as they could be if I had been suddenly transported
to another quarter of the globe. Their hair was carefully parted in the middle, combed behind the ears,
and tied behind in a long tail reaching a yard down
the back. The hair of this tail was firmly bound with
a long cord formed of monkeys' hair, very soft and
pliable. On the top of the head was stuck a comb, in-
geniously constructed of palm-wood and grass and ornamented with little tufts of toucans' rump feathers
at each end. The ears were pierced and a small piece
of straw stuck in the hole, altogether giving a most

feminine appearance to the face, increased by the total absence of beard or whiskers and by the hair of the eyebrows being almost entirely plucked out. A small strip of *tururi* (the inner bark of a tree) passed between the legs and secured to a string round the waist with a pair of knitted garters constituted their simple dress. . . .

We passed the night in the maloca, surrounded by the naked Indians hanging round their fires, which sent a fitful light up into the dark smoke-filled roof. A torrent of rain poured without, and I could not help admiring the degree of sociality and comfort in numerous families thus living together in patriarchal harmony. . . .

[At] a neighboring village . . . there was caxiri and dancing. . . . The regular festa had been broken up that morning; the chiefs and principal men had put off their feather headdresses, but as caxiri still remained, the young men and women continued dancing. . . .

The wild and strange appearance of these handsome, naked, painted Indians, with their curious ornaments and weapons, the stamp and song and rattle which accompanies the dance, the hum of conversation in a strange language, the music of fifes and flutes and other instruments of reed, bone, and turtles' shells, the large calabashes of caxiri constantly carried about, and the great smoke-blackened gloomy house, produced an effect to which no description can do justice and of which the sight of half a dozen Indians going through their dances for show gives but a very faint idea.

I stayed looking on a considerable time, highly delighted at such an opportunity of seeing these interesting people in their most characteristic festivals. I was myself a great object of admiration, principally on account of my spectacles, which they saw for the first time and could not at all understand.

AT TEFÉ ON THE UPPER AMAZON

[BATES] In the evening we arrived at a narrow opening . . . the mouth of the Tefé, on whose banks Tefé is situated, the termination of our voyage. After having struggled for thirty-five days with the muddy currents and insect pests of the Solimões, it was unspeakably refreshing to find one's self again in a dark-water river, smooth as a lake, and free from pium and motuca [two species of flies that torment the traveler]. . . .

I reflected on my own wandering life. I had now reached the end of the third stage of my journey and was now more than halfway across the continent. It was necessary for me, on many accounts, to find a rich locality for natural history explorations and settle myself in it for some months or years. Would the neighborhood of Tefé turn out to be suitable, and should I, a solitary stranger on a strange errand, find a welcome amongst its people? . . . A few days' experience of the people and the forest of the vicinity showed me that I might lay myself out for a long, pleasant, and busy residence at this place. . . .

I made Tefé my headquarters during the whole of the time I remained on the Upper Amazon (four years and a half). My excursions into the neighboring region extended sometimes as far as three and four hundred miles from the place . . . in the intervals between them I led a quiet, uneventful life in the settlement, following my pursuit in the same peaceful, regular way as a naturalist might do in a European village. For many weeks in succession my journal records little more than the notes made on my daily captures.

I had a dry and spacious cottage, the principal room of which was made a workshop and study; here a large table was placed, and my little library of reference arranged on shelves in rough wooden boxes. Cages for drying specimens were suspended from the rafters by cords well anointed, to prevent ants from descending, with a bitter vegetable oil: rats and mice were kept from them by inverted *cuias* [gourds], placed halfway down the cords. I always kept on hand a large portion of my private collection, which contained a pair of each species and variety, for the sake of comparing the old with the new acquisitions. . . .

I lived . . . on the best of terms with the inhabitants of Tefé. Refined society, of course, there was none, but the score or so of decent quiet families which constituted the upper class of the place were very sociable. . . . I was never troubled with that impertinent curiosity on the part of the people in these interior places which some travelers complain of in other countries. The Indians and lower half-castes —at least such of them who gave any thought to the subject—seemed to think it natural that strangers should collect and send abroad the beautiful birds and insects of their country. The butterflies they universally concluded to be wanted as patterns for bright-colored calico prints. As to the better sort of people, I had no difficulty in making them understand that each European capital had a public museum in which were sought to be stored specimens of all natural productions in the mineral, animal, and vegetable kingdoms. They could not comprehend how a man could study science for its own sake, but I told them I was collecting for the "Museo de Londres" and was paid for it, *that* was very intelligible. . . .

There were, of course, many drawbacks to the amenities of the place as a residence for a European, but these were not of a nature that my readers would perhaps imagine. There was scarcely any danger from wild animals. It seems almost ridiculous to refute the idea of danger from the natives in a country where even incivility to an unoffending stranger is a rarity. . . .

I suffered most inconvenience from the difficulty of getting news from the civilized world downriver, from the irregularity of receipt of letters, parcels of books and periodicals, and toward the latter part of my residence, from ill health arising from bad and insufficient food. The want of intellectual society and of the varied excitement of European life was also felt most acutely, and this, instead of becoming deadened by time, increased until it became almost insupportable. I was obliged at last to come to the conclusion that the contemplation of nature alone is not sufficient to fill the human heart and mind. . . .

We lived at Tefé during most of the year, on turtle. . . . Game of all kinds is scarce in the forest near the town, except in the months of June and July when immense numbers of a large and handsome bird, the white-throated toucan (*Ramphastos tucanus*) make their appearance. They come in well-fed condition, and are shot in such quantities that every family has the strange treat of stewed and roasted toucans daily for many weeks. Curassow birds are plentiful on the banks of the Solimões, but to get a brace or two requires the sacrifice of several days for the trip. A tapir, of which the meat is most delicious and nourishing, is sometimes killed by a fortunate hunter. I have still a lively recollection of the pleasant effects which I once experienced from a diet of fresh tapir meat for a few days after having been brought to a painful state of bodily and mental depression by a month's scanty rations of fish and farina....

The seasons in the Upper Amazon region offer some points of difference from those of the lower river and the district of Belém. . . . The year at Tefé is divided according to the rises and falls of the river with which coincide the wet and dry periods. All the principal transactions of life of the inhabitants are regulated by these yearly recurring phenomena. The peculiarity of this upper region consists in there being two rises and two falls within the year. . . . Thus the Tefé year is divided into four seasons, two of dry weather and falling waters and two of the reverse. Besides this variety there is in the month of May a short season of very cold weather, a most surprising circumstance in this otherwise uniformly sweltering climate. . . . The phenomenon, I presume, is to be accounted for by the fact that in May it is winter in the southern temperate zone and that the cool currents of air traveling thence northward toward the equator become only moderately heated in their course, owing to the intermediate country being a vast, partially-flooded plain covered with humid forests.

ALLIGATORS

I have hitherto had but few occasions of mentioning alligators, although they exist by myriads in the waters of the Upper Amazon. Many different species are spoken of by the natives. I saw only three, and of these two only are common: one, the jacare-tinga, a small kind (five feet long when full grown), having a long slender muzzle and a black-banded tail; the other, the jacaré-açu, to which these remarks more especially relate; and the third, the jacaré-curuá . . . or large caiman, [which] grows to a length of eighteen or twenty feet and attains an enormous bulk.

Like the turtles, the alligator has its annual migrations, for it retreats to the interior pools and flooded forests in the wet season and descends to the main river in the dry season. During the months of high water, therefore, scarcely a single individual is to be seen in the main river. In the middle part of the Lower Amazon, about Obidos and Parintins, where many of the lakes with their channels of communication with the trunk stream dry up in the fine months, the alligator buries itself in the mud and becomes dormant, sleeping till the rainy season returns. On the Upper Amazon, where the dry season is never excessive, it has not this habit, but is lively all the year round.

It is scarcely exaggerating to say that the waters of the Solimões are as well stocked with large alligators in the dry season as a ditch in England is in summer with tadpoles. During a journey of five days which I once made in the Upper Amazon steamer in November, alligators were seen along the coast almost every step of the way, and the passengers amused themselves from morning till night by firing at them with rifle and ball. They were very numerous in the still bays, where the huddled crowds jostled together, to the great rattling of their coats of mail, as the steamer passed.

The natives at once despise and fear the great caiman. I once spent a month at Alvarães, a small village of semicivilized Indians about twenty miles to the west of Tefé. My entertainer, the only white in the place and one of my best and most constant friends, Senhor Innocencio Alves Faria, one day proposed a half-day's fishing with net in the lake—the expanded bed of the small river on which the village is situated.

We set out in an open boat with six Indians and two of Innocencio's children. The water had sunk so low that the net had to be taken out into the middle by the Indians, whence at the first draft two medium-sized alligators were brought to land. They were disengaged from the net and allowed, with the coolest unconcern, to return to the water, although the two children were playing in it not many yards off. We continued fishing, Innocencio and I lending a helping hand, and each time drew a number of the reptiles of different ages and sizes, some of them jacaretingas. The lake in fact swarmed with alligators. . . .

[The alligator] never attacks man when his intended victim is on his guard, but he is cunning enough to know when this may be done with impunity. Of this we had proof at Alvarães a few days afterward. The river had sunk to a very low point, so that the port and bathing place of the village now lay at the foot of a long sloping bank, and a large caiman made his appearance in the shallow and muddy water. We were all obliged to be very careful in taking our bath, most of the people simply using a calabash, pouring the water over themselves while standing on the brink.

A large trading canoe, belonging to a Manaus merchant named Soares, arrived at this time, and the Indian crew as usual spent the first day or two after their coming into port in drunkenness and debauchery ashore. One of the men, during the greatest heat of the day, when almost everyone was enjoying his afternoon's nap, took it into his head whilst in a tipsy state to go down alone to bathe. He was seen only by the Juiz de Paz, a feeble old man who was lying in his hammock in the open veranda at the rear of his house on the top of the bank, and who shouted to the besotted Indian to beware of the alligator. Before he could repeat his warning, the man stumbled, and a pair of gaping jaws, appearing suddenly above the surface, seized him round the waist and drew him under the water. A cry of agony, "Ai Jesús!" was the last sign made by the wretched victim.

The village was aroused. The young men with praiseworthy readiness seized their harpoons and hurried down to the bank, but of course it was too late. A winding track of blood on the surface of the water was all that could be seen. They embarked, however, in montarias, determined on vengeance. The monster was traced, and when, after a short lapse of time, he came up to breathe—one leg of the man sticking out from his jaws—was dispatched with bitter curses.

5

THOUGHTS
AND THEORIES

. . . the wonderful variety and exquisite
beauty of the butterflies and birds, a variety and charm which grow upon one month
after month and year after year as ever
new and beautiful, strange and even mysterious forms are continually met with.

WALLACE, *My Life*

■ "The wonderful variety"—over and over again this
was impressed on Wallace and Bates from the beginning of their travels to the end. From the very first
they were almost overwhelmed by the numbers of
insects—not the numbers of individuals but the
numbers of different species. And everywhere they
turned, they came upon new ones.

The butterflies especially attracted their attention, partly because of their beauty and partly because
of some puzzling problems in identifying them. Bates
first came across a pair of mimetic butterflies not far
from Santarém, and he found many more as he went
westward into the humid and heavily forested region
of the Upper Amazon.

A mimetic butterfly is one which resembles, or mimics, a different species of butterfly. The similarity is only superficial, however, for the butterflies otherwise retain the basic characteristics of their original group, which is why they can still be properly identified. But this still leaves questions. Why, after all, *should* one species resemble another, and how could this have come about?

Bates's original solution to this puzzle has proved to be the correct one: that a rare, palatable butterfly is protected from predators by its superficial resemblance to a common unpalatable butterfly, when both inhabit the same area. It is a matter of protective coloration, in which an original similarity is increased by the process of natural selection.

And there was another kind of resemblance, the curious similarity between the hawkmoths and the hummingbirds. This similarity between unrelated animals is now known as "convergent evolution." As a naturalist Bates recognized that these animals belonged to different phyla, although their mode of life is similar. They both obtain their food by sipping nectar from flowers while in flight (although hummingbirds are active in the daytime and hawkmoths at night), and the resulting likeness in their actions and appearance leads the casual observer to think there is some direct relationship between them. But this is again only a superficial similarity. No protection is involved, nor do the animals necessarily inhabit the same area.

The local people, however, had their own explanation for this: that the hawkmoth turned into a hummingbird, somewhat like the metamorphosis of a caterpillar into a butterfly. (A similar sort of reasoning had misled Robert Chambers into thinking that new species could arise in this way, with one species giving birth directly to a completely different one.)

The fruits of the tropical forest are difficult to reach (their own protection from overexploitation), and animals have evolved various methods of coping with this problem. The toucan's enormous bill is one of them. Lamarck would have explained it in the same way that he explained the long neck of the giraffe—that it was the result of stretching to reach for food, the effects of this effort (the "acquired characteristics") then being passed on to the next generation. Natural selection, however, would presume that toucans' bills varied in size. The birds possessing larger ones could reach the fruit more easily, and they would be the ones to survive and reproduce their kind.

Besides the variety in the wildlife, there was wonderful variety even in the rivers, and these differences were often striking. One of the pleasant differences was the absence of mosquitoes on the black rivers, a happy circumstance that has only recently been explained. The decayed plant matter that colors these rivers contains hormonelike substances that interfere with the development of insects and act in effect as insecticides.

The rivers themselves contained many different forms of life. As Wallace traveled farther up the Rio Negro, the diversity of fishes caught his attention and he "began now to take a great interest in the beauty and variety of the species, and, whenever I could, made accurate drawings and descriptions of them." There were hundreds of different species in the Rio Negro and an uncounted number more in the Amazon. (More than fifteen hundred have now been described from the Amazon region.)

Wallace was one of the first to appreciate a special function of rivers, that they act as barriers to the distribution of many species of animals. Various things determine which animals are to be found where, but it is not always easy to find out what they are. Wallace discovered, however, that the ranges of monkeys were clearly bounded by the rivers. Some species were found only on the south side of the Amazon, others only on the north; still others were found only east or west of the Rio Negro.

Without a doubt, Wallace and Bates had chosen a good place to study "the variations, arrangements, distribution, etc., of species."

AN ABUNDANCE OF INSECTS

[BATES] The neighborhood of Belém is rich in insects. I do not speak of the number of individuals, which is probably less than one meets with, excepting ants and termites, in summer days in temperate latitudes; but the variety, or in other words, the number of species, is very great. It will convey some idea of the diversity of butterflies when I mention that about 700 species of that tribe are found within an hour's walk of the town; whilst the total number found in the British Islands does not exceed 66 and the whole of Europe supports only 321.

Some of the most showy species, such as the swallow-tailed kinds, *Papilio polycaon, thoas, torquatus,* and others, are seen flying about the streets and gardens; sometimes they come through the open windows, attracted by flowers in the apartments. These species of *Papilio* which are most characteristic of the country, so conspicuous in their velvety-black, green, and rose-colored hues, which Linnaeus, in pursuance of his elegant system of nomenclature—naming the different kinds after the heroes of Greek mythology—called trojans, never leave the shades of the forest. The splendid metallic-blue morphos, some of which measure seven inches in expanse, are generally confined to the shady alleys of the forest. They sometimes come forth into the broad sunlight. When we first went to look at our new residence in Nazareth, a *Morpho menelaus,* one of the most beautiful kinds, was seen flapping its huge wings like a bird along the veranda.

This species, however, although much admired, looks dull in color by the side of its congener, the *Morpho rhetenor,* whose wings, on the upper face, are of quite a dazzling luster. *Rhetenor* usually prefers the broad sunny roads in the forest, and is an almost unattainable prize on account of its lofty flight, for it very rarely descends nearer the ground than about twenty feet. When it comes sailing along, it occasionally flaps its wings, and then the blue surface flashes in the sunlight, so that it is visible a quarter of a mile off. There is another species of this genus, of a satiny-white hue, the *Morpho uraneis.* This is equally difficult to obtain; the male only has the satiny luster, the female being of a pale-lavender color.

It is in the height of the dry season that the greatest number and variety of butterflies are found in the woods, especially when a shower falls at intervals of a few days. An infinite number of curious and rare species may then be taken, most diversified in habits, mode of flight, colors, and markings: some yellow, others bright red, green, purple, and blue, and many bordered or spangled with metallic lines and spots of a silvery or golden luster. Some have wings transparent as glass. One of these clearwings is especially beautiful, namely the *Hetaira esmeralda*. It has one spot only of opaque coloring on its wings, which is of a violet and rose hue; this is the only part visible when the insect is flying low over dead leaves in the gloomy shades where alone it is found, and it then looks like a wandering petal of a flower.

Bees and wasps are not especially numerous near Belém. . . . Many species of *Mygale,* those monstrous hairy spiders, half a foot in expanse, which attract the attention so much in museums, are found in sandy places at Nazareth. The different kinds have the most diversified habits. Some construct, amongst the tiles or thatch of houses, dens of closely woven web, which in texture very much resemble fine muslin; these are often seen crawling over the walls of apartments. Others build similar nests in trees, and are known to attack birds.

One very robust fellow burrows into the earth, forming a broad, slanting gallery about two feet long, the sides of which he lines beautifully with silk. He is nocturnal in his habits. Just before sunset he may be seen keeping watch within the mouth of his tunnel, disappearing suddenly when he hears a heavy foot-tread near his hiding place. The number of spiders ornamented with showy colors was somewhat remarkable. Some double themselves up at the base of leaf stalks so as to resemble flower buds and thus deceive the insects on which they prey. . . .

Coleoptera, or beetles, at first seemed very

scarce. This apparent scarcity has been noticed in other equatorial countries, and arises, probably, from the great heat of the sun not permitting them to exist in exposed positions, where they form such conspicuous objects in Europe. Many hundred species of the different families can be found when they are patiently searched for in the shady places to which they are confined. It is vain to look for carnivorous beetles under stones, or anywhere, indeed, in open, sunny places.

The terrestrial forms of this interesting family, which abound in England and temperate countries generally, are scarce in the neighborhood of Belém—in fact I met with only four or five species; on the other hand the purely arboreal kinds were rather numerous. The contrary of this happens in northern latitudes, where the great majority of the species and genera are exclusively terrestrial. The arboreal forms are distinguished by the structure of their feet, which have broad spongy soles and toothed claws enabling them to climb over and cling to branches and leaves. The remarkable scarcity of ground beetles is doubtless attributable to the number of ants and termites which people every inch of surface in all shady places and which would most likely destroy the larvae of Coleoptera. Moreover, these active creatures have the same functions as Coleoptera, and thus render their existence unnecessary.

The large proportion of climbing forms of carnivorous beetles is an interesting fact because it affords another instance of the arboreal character which animal forms tend to assume in equinoctial America, a circumstance which points to the slow adaptation of the fauna to a forest-clad country throughout an immense lapse of geological time.

MIMETIC BUTTERFLIES

. . . One of the most conspicuous insects peculiar to Parintins is an exceedingly handsome butterfly which has been named *Agrias phalcidon*. It is of large size, and the colors of the upper surface of its wings resemble those of the *Callithea leprieurii* . . . dark blue with a broad silvery-green border. When it settles on leaves of trees, fifteen or twenty feet from the ground, it closes its wings and then exhibits a row of brilliant pale-blue eyelike spots with white pupils, which adorns their under surface. Its flight is exceedingly swift, but when at rest it is not easily made to budge from its place; or if driven off, returns soon after to the same spot. Its superficial resemblance to *Callithea leprieurii*, which is a very abundant species in the same locality, is very close.

The likeness might be considered a mere accidental coincidence, especially as it refers chiefly to the upper surface of the wings, if similar parallel resemblances did not occur between other species of the same two genera. Thus on the Upper Amazon another totally distinct kind of *Agrias* mimics still more closely another *Callithea*, both insects being peculiar to the district where they are found flying together.

Resemblances of this nature are very numerous in the insect world. I was much struck with them in the course of my travels, especially when, on removing from one district to another, local varieties of certain species were found accompanied by local varieties of the species which counterfeited them in the former locality, under a dress changed to correspond with the altered liveries of the species they mimicked. One cannot help concluding these imitations to be intentional and that nature has some motive in their production.

In many cases the reason of the imitation is sufficiently plain. For instance, when a fly or parasitic bee has a deceptive resemblance to the species of working bee in whose nest it deposits the egg it has otherwise no means of providing for, or when a leaping spider, as it crouches in the axil of a leaf waiting for its prey, presents an exact imitation of a flower bud, it is evident that the benefit of the imitating species is the object had in view.

When, however, an insect mimics another species of its own order where predaceous or parasitic habits are out of the question, it is not so easy to divine the precise motive of the adaptation. We may be sure, nevertheless, that one of the two is assimilated in external appearance to the other for some purpose useful—perhaps of life and death importance—to the species.

I believe these imitations are of the same nature as those in which an insect or lizard is colored and marked so as to resemble the soil, leaf, or bark on which it lives, the resemblance serving to conceal the creatures from the prying eyes of their enemies, or if they are predaceous species, serving them as a disguise to enable them to approach their prey. When an insect, instead of a dead or inorganic substance, mimics another species of its own order, and does not prey or is not parasitic, may it not be inferred that the mimicker is subject to a persecution by insectivorous animals from which its model is free? Many species of insects have a most deceptive resemblance

to living or dead leaves. It is generally admitted that
this serves to protect them from the onslaughts of in-
sect-feeding animals who would devour the insect but
refuse the leaf. The same might be said of a species
mimicking another of the same order; one may be as
repugnant to the tastes of insect persecutors as a leaf
or a piece of bark would be, and its imitator not enjoying this advantage would escape by being decep-
tively assimilated to it in external appearances.

In the present instance, it is not very clear what
property the *Callithea* possesses to render it less liable
to persecution than the *Agrias,* except it be that it has
a strong odor somewhat resembling vanilla which the
Agrias is destitute of. This odor becomes very powerful when the insect is roughly handled or pinched,
and if it serves as a protection to the *Callithea,* it
would explain why the *Agrias* is assimilated to it in
colors. The resemblance, as before remarked, applies
chiefly to the upper side; in other species it is equally
close on both surfaces of the wings. Some birds, and
the great *Aeschna* dragonflies, take their insect prey
whilst on the wing, when the upper surface of the
wings is the side most conspicuous.

HUMMINGBIRDS AND HAWKMOTHS

In January the orange trees became covered with
blossom—at least to a greater extent than usual, for
they flower more or less in this country all the year
round—and the flowers attracted a great number of
hummingbirds. Every day, in the cooler hours of the
morning and in the evening from four o'clock till six,
they were to be seen whirring about the trees by

scores. Their motions are unlike those of all other birds. They dart to and fro so swiftly that the eye can scarcely follow them, and when they stop before a flower it is only for a few moments. They poise themselves in an unsteady manner, their wings moving with inconceivable rapidity, probe the flower, and then shoot off to another part of the tree. They do not proceed in that methodical manner which bees follow, taking the flowers seriatim, but skip about from one part of the tree to another in the most capricious way. Sometimes two males close with each other and fight, mounting upward in the struggle, as insects are often seen to do when similarly engaged, and then separating hastily and darting back to their work. Now and then they stop to rest, perching on leafless twigs, where they may be sometimes seen probing, from the places where they sit, the flowers within their reach.

The brilliant colors with which they are adorned cannot be seen whilst they are fluttering about, nor can the different species be distinguished unless they have a deal of white hue in their plumage, such as *Heliothryx aurita,* which is wholly white underneath although of a glittering green color above, and the white-tailed *Florisuga mellivora.* There is not a great variety of hummingbirds in the Amazon region, the number of species being far smaller in these uniform forest plains than in the diversified valleys of the Andes under the same parallels of latitude.

The family is divisible into two groups contrasted in form and habits, one containing species which live entirely in the shade of the forest and the other comprising those which prefer open sunny places. The forest species are seldom seen at flowers, flowers being, in the shady places where they abide, of rare occurrence; but they search for insects on leaves, threading the bushes and passing above and beneath each leaf with wonderful rapidity. The other group are not quite confined to cleared places, as they come into the forest whenever a tree is in blossom and descend into sunny openings where flowers are to be found. But it is only where the woods are less dense than usual that this is the case; in the lofty forests and twilight shades of the lowlands and islands they are scarcely ever seen. . . .

Several times I shot by mistake a hummingbird hawkmoth instead of a bird. This moth is somewhat smaller than hummingbirds generally are, but its manner of flight and the way it poises itself before a flower whilst probing it with its proboscis are precisely like the same actions of hummingbirds. It was only after many days' experience that I learned to distinguish one from the other when on the wing. This resemblance has attracted the notice of the natives, all of whom, even educated whites, firmly believe that one is transmutable into the other. They have observed the metamorphosis of caterpillars into butterflies and think it not at all more wonderful that a moth should change into a hummingbird.

The resemblance between this hawkmoth and a hummingbird is certainly very curious, and strikes one even when both are examined in the hand. Holding them sideways, the shape of the head and position of the eyes in the moth are seen to be nearly the same as in the bird, the extended proboscis representing the long beak. At the tip of the moth's body there is a brush of long hair-scales resembling feathers, which, being expanded, looks very much like a bird's tail. But of course all these points of resemblance are merely superficial.

The Negroes and Indians tried to convince me that the two were of the same species. "Look at their feathers," they said, "their eyes are the same and so are their tails." This belief is so deeply rooted that it was usless to reason with them on the subject. The *Macroglossa* moths are found in most countries, and have everywhere the same habits; one well-known species is found in England. . . . The analogy between the two creatures has been brought about, probably, by the similarity of their habits, there being no indication of the one having been adapted in outward appearance with reference to the other.

THE TOUCAN'S BILL

Flowers and fruit on the crowns of the large trees of South American forests grow principally toward the end of slender twigs which will not bear any considerable weight; all animals, therefore, which feed upon fruit or on insects contained in flowers must, of course, have some means of reaching the ends of the stalks from a distance. Monkeys obtain their food by stretching forth their long arms, and in some instances their tails, to bring the fruit near to their mouths. Hummingbirds are endowed with highly perfected organs of flight, with corresponding muscular development, by which they are enabled to sustain themselves on the wing before blossoms whilsts rifling them of their contents. These strong-flying creatures, however, will, whenever they can get near enough, remain on their perches whilst probing neighboring flowers for insects.

Trogons have feeble wings and a dull, inactive temperament. Their mode of obtaining food is to station themselves quietly on low branches in the gloomy shades of the forest and eye the fruits on the surrounding trees, darting off, as if with an effort, every time they wish to seize a mouthful, and returning to the same perch. Barbets (Capitonidae) seem to have no especial endowment, either of habits or structure, to enable them to seize fruits; and in this respect they are similar to the toucans, if we leave the bill out of the question, both tribes having heavy bodies, with feeble organs of flight so that they are disabled from taking their food on the wing.

The purpose of the enormous bill [of the toucan] here becomes evident. It is to enable the toucan to reach and devour fruit whilst remaining seated, and thus to counterbalance the disadvantage which its heavy body and gluttonous appetite would otherwise give it in the competition with allied groups of birds. The relation between the extraordinarily lengthened bill of the toucan and its mode of obtaining food is therefore precisely similar to that between the long neck and lips of the giraffe and the mode of browsing of the animal.

The bill of the toucan can scarcely be considered a very perfectly formed instrument for the end to which it is applied, as here explained, but nature appears not to invent organs at once for the functions to which they are now adapted, but avails herself, here of one already existing structure or instinct, there of another, according as they are handy when need for their further modification arises.

THE RIVERS OF THE AMAZON BASIN

[WALLACE] . . . I had a good opportunity of observing the striking difference between this river [the Rio Negro] and the Amazon. Here were no islands of floating grass, no logs and uprooted trees with their cargoes of gulls, scarcely any stream, and few signs of life in the black and sluggish waters. Yet when there is a storm, there are greater and more dangerous waves than on the Amazon. When the dark clouds above cause the water to appear of a yet more inky blackness and the rising waves break in white foam over the vast expanse, the scene is gloomy in the extreme.

At Manaus the river is about a mile and a half wide. A few miles up it widens considerably, in many places forming deep bays eight or ten miles across. Farther on again it separates into several channels divided by innumerable islands, and the total width is probably not less than twenty miles. . . .

The numerous tributary streams of the Amazon, many of them equal to the largest rivers of Europe, differ remarkably in the color of their waters, the character of the vegetation on their banks and the animals that inhabit them. They may be divided into three groups—the white-water rivers, the blue-water rivers, and the black-water rivers.

The main stream of the Amazon itself is a white-water river, this name being applied to those waters which are of a pale yellowish-olive color. . . .

The waters of the Amazon continue of the same color up to the mouth the Ucayali [in Peru], when they become blue or transparent. . . . The difference of color between the white- and blue-water rivers is evidently owing to the nature of the country they flow through: a rocky or sandy district will always have clear-water rivers; an alluvial or clayey one will have yellow or olive-colored streams. . . .

All the rivers that rise in the mountains of Brazil have blue or clear water. The Tocantins, the Xingú, and the Tapajoz are the chief of this class. The Tocantins runs over volcanic and crystalline rocks in the lower parts of its course and its waters are beautifully transparent. . . . The Tapajoz, which enters the Amazon about five hundred miles above Belém, is clear to its mouth and forms a striking contrast to the yellow flood of that river.

It is above the Madeira that we first meet with the curious phenomenon of great rivers of black water. The Rio Negro is the largest and most celebrated of these. . . .

On the south of the Amazon there are also some black-water streams—the Coari, the Tefé, the Juruá, and some others. The inhabitants have taken advantage of these to escape from the plague of mosquitoes, and the towns of Coari and Tefé are places of refuge for the traveler on the Upper Amazon, those annoying insects being scarcely ever found on the black waters.

The causes of the peculiar color of these rivers are not, I think, very obscure. It appears to me to be produced by the solution of decaying leaves, roots, and other vegetable matter. In the virgin forests, in which most of these streams have their source, the little brooks and rivulets are half choked up with dead leaves and rotten branches, giving various brown tinges to the water. When these rivulets meet together and accumulate into a river, they of course have a deep-brown hue. . . . The Rio Negro . . .

and several other smaller rivers have their sources and their whole course in the deep forest; they flow generally over clean granite rocks and beds of sand, and their streams are gentle, so as not to wear away the soft parts of their banks.

The Ica, Japurá, and Upper Amazon, on the contrary, flow through a long extent of alluvial country, and having their sources on the slopes of the Andes, are much more liable to sudden floods, and by their greater velocity bring down a quantity of sediment.

As might be expected in the greatest river in the world, there is a corresponding abundance and variety of fish. They supply the Indians with the greater part of their animal food and are at all times more plentiful and easier to be obtained than birds or game from the forest.

During my residence on the Rio Negro I carefully figured and described every species I met with, and at the time I left, fresh ones were every day occurring. The soft-finned fishes are much the most numerous, and comprise some of the best kinds of food. . . .

Of all kinds of fishes I found two hundred and five species in the Rio Negro alone, and these, I am sure, are but a small portion of what exist there. Being a black-water river, most of its fishes are different from those found in the Amazon. In fact, in every small river, and in different parts of the same river, distinct kinds are found. The greater part of those which inhabit the upper Rio Negro are not found near its mouth, where there are many other kinds equally unknown in the clearer, darker, and probably colder waters of its higher branches.

From the number of new fishes constantly found in every fresh locality and in every fisherman's basket, we may estimate that at least five hundred species exist in the Rio Negro and its tributary streams. The number in the whole valley of the Amazon it is impossible to estimate with any approach to accuracy.

GEOGRAPHICAL DISTRIBUTION OF ANIMALS

There is no part of natural history more interesting or instructive than the study of the geographical distribution of animals.

It is well known that countries possessing a climate and soil very similar may differ almost entirely in their productions. Thus Europe and North America have scarcely an animal in common in the temperate zone, and South America contrasts equally with the opposite coast of Africa, while Australia differs almost entirely in its productions from districts under the same parallel of latitude in South Africa and South America. In all these cases there is a wide extent of sea separating the countries, which few animals can pass over; so that, supposing the animal productions to have been originally distinct, they could not well have become intermixed.

In each of these countries we find well-marked smaller districts, appearing to depend upon climate. The tropical and temperate parts of America and Africa have, generally speaking, distinct animals in each of them.

On a more minute acquaintance with the animals of any country, we shall find that they are broken up into yet smaller local groups, and that almost every district has peculiar animals found nowhere else. Great mountain chains are found to separate countries possessing very distinct sets of animals. Those of the east and west of the Andes differ very remarkably. The Rocky Mountains also separate two distinct zoological districts, California and Oregon on the one side, possessing plants, birds, and insects not found in any part of North America east of that range.

But there must be many other kinds of boundaries besides these, which, independently of climate, limit the range of animals. Places not more than fifty or a hundred miles apart often have species of insects and birds at the one which are not found at the other. There must be some boundary which determines the range of each species, some external peculiarity to mark the line which each one does not pass.

These boundaries do not always form a barrier to the progress of the animal, for many birds have a limited range in a country where there is nothing to prevent them flying in every direction—as in the case of the nightingale, which is quite unknown in some of our western counties. Rivers generally do not determine the distribution of species, because, when small, there are few animals which cannot pass them; but in very large rivers the case is different, and they will, it is believed, be found to be the limits, determining the range of many animals of all orders.

With regard to the Amazon and its larger tributaries, I have ascertained this to be the case, and shall here mention the facts which tend to prove it.

During my residence in the Amazon district I took every opportunity of determining the limits of species, and I soon found that the Amazon, the Rio Negro and the Madeira formed the limits beyond which certain species [of monkeys] never passed. The native hunters are perfectly acquainted with this fact, and always cross over the river when they want to procure particular animals which are found even on the river's bank on one side, but never by any chance on the other. On approaching the sources of the rivers they cease to be a boundary, and most of the species are found on both sides of them.

Thus several Guiana species come up to the Rio Negro and Amazon, but do not pass them; Brazilian species on the contrary reach but do not pass the Amazon to the north. Several Ecuador species from the east of the Andes reach down into the tongue of land between the Rio Negro and Upper Amazon, but pass neither of these rivers, and others from Peru are bounded on the north by the Upper Amazon and on the east by the Madeira.

These facts are, I think, sufficient to prove that these rivers do accurately limit the range of some species, and in the cases just mentioned, the evidence is the more satisfactory because monkeys are animals so well known to the native hunters, they are so much sought after for food and all their haunts are so thoroughly searched, and the localities for the separate kinds are so often the subject of communication from one hunter to another, that it is quite impossible that any well-known species can exist in a particular district unknown to men whose lives are occupied in forming an acquaintance with the various tenants of the forests.

6
HOME

. . . I took a last view of the glorious forest for which I had so much love, and to explore which I had devoted so many years.
BATES, *Naturalist on the Amazons*

■ Wallace returned to England almost seven years before Bates did. His last expedition in South America was his second dangerous ascent of the Uaupés River. Serious illness had delayed him for three precious months and he missed the best collecting season there. He did not reach his goal either, but stopped a week short of it at Mitú, then the tiny Indian village of Mucura. Nevertheless, impractical as such a project may seem, he did succeed in acquiring a large collection of live animals that he planned to take back to England.

He started from Mitú, nearly two thousand miles from the Atlantic Ocean, at the end of March 1852, and he finally arrived home in the following Oc-

tober after an absence of nearly four and a half years.
But the ship on which he sailed had caught fire and
sunk, and now most of what he had hoped to gain
from those years of labor, including the live animals
and collections he had found still unshipped at
Manaus, was at the bottom of the ocean.

Although Wallace and his companions were res-
cued, Wallace's losses were devasting. He did not
have his private collections at hand to study as he had
expected, and this necessarily limited his writing. Furthermore he needed the money from the sale of lost
specimens. But he was not discouraged. He solved
this new predicament in a characteristic way—he
would make another trip, this time to the Far East.

THOUGHTS OF HOME

[WALLACE] From what I had seen on this river [the
Uaupés], there is no place equal to it for procuring a
fine collection of live birds and animals. This, together with the desire to see more of a country so interesting and so completely unknown, induced me,
after mature deliberation, to give up for the present
my intended journey to the Andes and to substitute
another voyage up the river Uaupés, at least to the
Jurupari (Devil) cataract, the "ultima Thule" of
most of the traders and about a month's voyage up
from its mouth. . . . These four months [Novem-
ber to February] I hoped, therefore, to spend there,
so as to be able to descend to Manaus, and thence to
Belém, in time to return to England by July or August with a numerous and valuable collection of live
animals. It was on account of these principally that I

determined to return to England a year before the time I had fixed upon, as it was impossible to send them without personal care and attendance.

And so, having once made up my mind to this course, with what delight I thought upon the sweets of home! What a paradise did that distant land seem to me! How I thought of the many simple pleasures, so long absent—the green fields, the pleasant woods, the flowery paths, the neat gardens—all so unknown here! What visions of the fireside did I conjure up of the social tea table with familiar faces around it! What a luxury seemed simple bread and butter!—and to think that perhaps in one short year I might be in the midst of all this! There was a pleasure in the mere thought that made me leap over the long months, the weary hours, the troubles and annoyances of tedious journeys that had first to be endured. I passed hours in solitary walks thinking of home; and never did I in former years long to be away in this tropic land with half the earnestness with which I now looked forward to returning back again.

A DISASTROUS VOYAGE

On the 25th [of March 1852], having been just a fortnight at Mitú, I left, much disappointed with regard to the collections I had made there. . . . I was still too weak to go out into the forest, and besides, had my live stock to attend to, which now consisted of four monkeys, about a dozen parrots, and six or eight small birds. It was a constant trouble to get food for them in suffecent variety and to prevent them from escaping. Most of the birds are brought up without being confined, and if placed in a cage, attempt constantly to get out and refuse food till they die. If, on the other hand, they are loose, they wander about to the Indians' houses or into the forest, and are often lost. . . .

The fever and ague now attacked me again, and I passed several days very uncomfortably. We had almost constant rains; and to attend to my numerous birds and animals was a great annoyance, owing to the crowded state of the canoe and the impossibility of properly cleaning them during the rain. Some died almost every day, and I often wished I had had nothing whatever to do with them, though having once taken them in hand, I determined to persevere. . . . We had plenty more rain every night, making the journey very disagreeable, and at length, on the 17th [of May] reached Manaus. . . .

At length the canoe arrived in which I was to go to Belém, and I soon agreed for my passage and set to work getting my things together. I had a great number of cases and boxes, six large ones which I had left with Senhor Henrique [an Italian and the principal merchant of Manaus] the year before being still in his possession, because the great men of Manaus were afraid they might contain contraband articles and would not let them pass.

I now got them embarked by making a declaration of their contents and paying a small duty on them. Out of a hundred live animals which I had purchased or had had given to me, there now only remained thirty-four, consisting of five monkeys, two macaws, twenty parrots and parakeets of twelve different species, five small birds, a crested bobwhite, and a toucan.

On the 10th of June we left Manaus, commencing our voyage very unfortunately for me; for on going on board after bidding adieu to my friends, I missed my toucan, which had no doubt flown overboard, and not being noticed by any one, was drowned. This bird I esteemed very highly, as he was full grown and very tame, and I had great hopes of bringing him alive to England. . . .

At length, on the 2nd of July, we reached Belém . . . and [I] was glad to learn that there was a vessel in port that would probably sail for London in about a week.

I agreed for my passage in the brig *Helen*, two hundred and thirty-five tons, Captain John Turner, whose property she was; and on the morning of Monday, the 12th of July, we got aboard and bade adieu to the white houses and waving palm trees of Belém. Our cargo consisted of about a hundred and twenty tons of India rubber and a quantity of cocoa, arnatto [a plant dye], piassava [palm fibers], and balsam of capivi [resinous substance used mostly in lacquers and varnishes]. . . . For three weeks we had very light winds and fine weather, and on the 6th of August had reached about latitude 30° 30′ north, longitude 52° west.

On that morning, after breakfast, I was reading in the cabin when the captain came down and said to me, "I'm afraid the ship's on fire; come and see what you think of it." . . .

Seeing that there was now little chance of our being able to extinguish the fire, the captain thought it prudent to secure our own safety, and called all hands to get out the boats and such necessaries as we should want in case of being obliged to take them.

. . . I went down into the cabin, now suffocatingly hot and full of smoke, to see what was worth saving. I got my watch and a small tin box containing some shirts and a couple of old notebooks with some drawings of plants and animals, and scrambled up with them on deck. Many clothes and a large portfolio of drawings and sketches remained in my berth, but I did not care to venture down again, and in fact felt a kind of apathy about saving anything that I can now hardly account for. . . .

There was now a scorching heat on the quarter-deck, and we saw that all hope was over and that we must in a few minutes be driven by the terrible element to take refuge on the scarcely less dangerous one which heaved and swelled its mighty billows a thousand miles on every side of us. The captain at length ordered all into the boats, and was himself the last to leave the vessel. . . .

Night was now coming on. The whole deck was a mass of fire, giving out an intense heat. We determined to stay by the vessel all night, as the light would attract any ship passing within a considerable distance of us. . . .

At length morning came; the dangers of the night were past, and with hopeful hearts we set up our little masts and rigged our sails, and bidding adieu to the still burning wreck of our ship, went gaily bounding alone before a light east wind. And then pencils and books were hunted out and our course and distance to Bermuda calculated; and we found that this, the nearest point of land in the vast waste of waters round us, was at least seven hundred miles away. But still we went on full of hope, for the wind was fair and we reckoned that if it did not change, we might make a hundred miles a day, and so in seven days reach the longed-for haven. . . .

On the 13th the wind was due west, blowing exactly from the point we wanted to go to. . . . We had now been a week in the boats and were only halfway to the islands, so we put all hands on short allowance of water before it was too late. The sun was very hot and oppressive and we suffered much from thirst. . . .

On the 15th the wind again died away and we had another calm. . . . We were almost in despair about seeing a ship or getting on to the islands. At about 5:00 P.M. . . . we saw a vessel coming nearly toward us and only about five miles distant. We were saved! . . .

That night I could not sleep. Home and all its pleasures seemed now within my grasp; and crowding thoughts, and hopes and fears, made me pass a more restless night than I should have done had we still been in the boats with diminishing hopes of rescue. The ship was the *Jordeson*, Captain Venables, from Cuba, bound for London with a cargo of mahogany, fustic, and other woods. We were picked up in latitude 32° 48′ north, longitude 60° 27′ west, being still about two hundred miles from Bermuda.

For several days afterward we had fine weather and very light winds, and went creeping along about fifty miles a day. It was now, when the danger appeared past, that I began to feel fully the greatness of my loss. With what pleasure had I looked upon every rare and curious insect I had added to my collection! How many times, when almost overcome by the ague, had I crawled into the forest and been rewarded by some unknown and beautiful species! How many places which no European foot but my own had trod-

den would have been recalled to my memory by the
rare birds and insects they had furnished to my collection! How many weary days and weeks had I
passed, upheld only by the fond hope of bringing
home many new and beautiful forms from those wild
regions; every one of which would be endeared to me
by the recollections they would call up, which should
prove that I had not wasted the advantages I had enjoyed and would give me occupation and amusement
for many years to come! And now everything was
gone, and I had not one specimen to illustrate the
unknown lands I had trod or to call back the recollection of the wild scenes I had beheld! But such regrets
I knew were vain, and I tried to think as little as possible about what might have been and to occupy myself with the state of things which actually existed.

We were in the [English] Channel on the 29th
of September when a violent gale occurred that did
great damage to the shipping and caused the destruction of many vessels much more seaworthy than our
own. The next morning we had four feet of water in
the hold.

On the 1st of October the pilot came on board.

October 1. Oh, glorious day! Here we are on
shore at Deal, where the ship is at anchor. Such a
dinner with our two captains! Oh, beefsteaks and
damson tart, a paradise for hungry sinners. . . .

October 5. London. . . . How I begin to envy
you in that glorious country where "the sun shines
for ever unchangeably bright," where farina abounds
and of bananas and plantains there is no lack! Fifty
times since I left Belém have I vowed, if I once
reached England, never to trust myself more on the
ocean. But good resolutions soon fade, and I am al-

ready only doubtful whether the Andes or the Philippines are to be the scene of my next wanderings.

However, for six months I am a fixture here in London, as I am determined to make up for lost time by enjoying myself as much as possible for a while. I am fortunate in having £200 insured by Mr. Stevens' foresight, so I must be contented, though it is very hard to have nothing to show of what I took so much pains to procure.

SALVAGE

In the small tin box which I had saved from the wreck I fortunately had a set of careful pencil drawings of all the different species of palms I had met with, together with notes as to their distribution and uses. I had also a large number of drawings of fish . . . carefully made to scale, with notes of their colors, their dentition, and their fin rays, scales, etc. I had also a folio Portuguese notebook containing my diary while on the Rio Negro, and some notes and observations made for a map of that river and the Uaupés.

With these scanty materials, helped by the letters I had sent home, I now set to work to write an account of my travels as well as a few scientific papers for which I had materials in the portion of my collections made in Belém, Santarém, and the lower Rio Negro. These I had sent off before leaving Manaus on my first voyage up the Rio Negro, and they had arrived home safely, but I had reserved all my private collections for comparison with future discoveries, and though I left these to be sent home before starting on my second voyage up the Rio Negro, they were never dispatched, owing to the custom house authorities at Manaus insisting on seeing the contents before allowing them to go away. I therefore found them at Manaus on my way home, and they were all lost with the ship.

THE NEXT VENTURE

During my constant attendance at the meetings of the Zoological and Entomological societies and visits to the insect and bird departments of the British Museum, I had obtained sufficient information to satisfy me that the very finest field for an exploring and collecting naturalist was to be found in the great Malayan Archipelago, of which just sufficient was known to prove its wonderful richness, while no part of it, with the one exception of the island of Java, had been well explored as regards its natural history.

Sir James Brooke had recently become rajah of Sarawak, while the numerous Dutch settlements in Celebes and the Moluccas offered great facilities for a traveler. So far as known also, the country was generally healthy, and I determined that it would be much better for me to go to such a new country than to return to the Amazon, where Bates had already been successfully collecting for five years, and where I knew there was a good bird collector who had been long at work in the upper part of the river toward the Andes.

■ On his way back down the Amazon, Wallace had just missed meeting Bates, then headquartered at Santarém. Bates remained there until 1855, and then returned to the Upper Amazon. He had hoped to continue his explorations up into Peru, but ill health forced him to abandon this plan, and the farthest point that he reached was São Paulo de Olivença, more than a hundred miles from the border.

Bates returned to Belém for the last time in March 1859, to discover with some sadness that many changes had taken place since his arrival eleven years before. He was particularly distressed by the cutting of the forest. Unfortunately, this has continued to the present day, and the magnificent forests of the Amazon Basin are in danger of being thoughtlessly destroyed.

Finally, on June 2, 1859, Bates "left Belém, probably forever." He divided his priceless private collections into three parts and sent them home on three different ships to avoid the catastrophe that had befallen Wallace. All arrived safely in England, and Bates's mission was successfully accomplished.

The collections from this "naturalist's paradise" were enormous, and they made a valuable contribution to scientific knowledge. But it must be remembered that Bates (and Wallace) traveled more than a hundred years ago, usually alone, and in an almost undisturbed and unknown forest. Then, there would have been little if any damage to rare species in the small number of specimens collected by a few daring men.

Present-day collectors must take a different view, for the forest and its multitude of species are endangered by man and his activities. Tropical regions must be studied, not destroyed, and collectors themselves must beware of contributing to the disappearance of the very rarities they seek.

Bates was successful in other ways as well. With his collections of insects on hand, he was able to study them at leisure, and he worked out, among other things, his famous theory of mimicry. He had the further advantage that by then the theory of natural selection had already been proposed by Darwin and Wallace, and he was able to incorporate it in his work. His publications attracted the attention of the scientific world, and he soon came to know some of the leading figures, including Hooker and Darwin. It was Darwin, in fact, who encouraged him to write of his travels, and his book, a happy blend of science and adventure, is still considered one of the best of the period.

Like Wallace, Bates had hoped to escape from the drudgery of his former life, and here again he succeeded. In 1864 he was appointed assistant secretary of the Royal Geographical Society in London, a full-time job which he held until his death in 1892. (By a coincidence, Wallace was his only competitor for this position.) He advised other explorers, helped them with their own publications, and edited the *Transactions* of the Society—a quieter life than Wallace's was to be and less in the limelight, but a satisfying outcome, nevertheless, to the years of struggle.

NEAR THE PERUVIAN BORDER

[BATES] I remained at São Paulo five months; five years would not have been sufficient to exhaust the treasures of its neighborhood in zoology and botany. Although now a forest rambler of ten years' experience, the beautiful forest which surrounds this settlement gave me as much enjoyment as if I had only just landed for the first time in a tropical country.

The plateau on which the village is built extends

on one side nearly a mile into the forest, but on the other side the descent into the lowland begins close to the streets; the hill sloping abruptly toward a boggy meadow surrounded by woods, through which a narrow winding path continues the slope down to a cool shady glen, with a brook of icy-cold water flowing at the bottom. At midday the vertical sun penetrates into the gloomy depths of this romantic spot, lighting up the leafy banks of the rivulet and its clean sandy margins, where numbers of scarlet, green, and black tanagers and brightly colored butterflies sport about in the stray beams.

Sparkling brooks, large and small, traverse the glorious forest in almost every direction, and one is constantly meeting, whilst rambling through the thickets, with trickling rills and bubbling springs, so well provided is the country with moisture. Some of the rivulets flow over a sandy and pebbly bed, and the banks of all are clothed with the most magnificent vegetation conceivable. I had the almost daily habit, in my solitary walks, of resting on the clean banks of these swift-flowing streams and bathing for an hour at a time in their bracing waters—hours which now remain amongst my most pleasant memories.

The broad forest roads continue, as I was told, a distance of several days' journey into the interior, which is peopled by Tucunas and other Indians living in scattered houses and villages nearly in their primitive state, the nearest village lying about six miles from São Paulo. The banks of all the streams are dotted with palm-thatched dwellings of Tucunas, all half buried in the leafy wilderness, the scattered families having chosen the coolest and shadiest nooks for their abodes. . . .

In the fourth month of my sojourn at São Paulo I had a serious illness, an attack of the *sezão,* or ague of the country, which as it left me with shattered health and dampened enthusiasm, led to my abandoning the plan I had formed of proceeding to the Peruvian towns of Pebas and Moyobamba, two hundred and fifty and six hundred miles further west, and so completing the examination of the natural history of the Amazonian plains up to the foot of the Andes.

I made a very large collection at São Paulo, and employed a collector at Sapurara and on the banks of the Javari for several months, so that I acquired a very fair knowledge altogether of the productions of the country bordering the Amazon to the end of the Brazilian territory, a distance of nineteen hundred miles from the Atlantic at the mouth of the Pará. But beyond the Peruvian boundary I found now I should be unable to go.

My ague seemed to be the culmination of a gradual deterioration of health which had been going on for several years. I had exposed myself too much in the sun, working to the utmost of my strength six days a week, and had suffered much besides from bad and insufficient food. . . . When the steamer ascended in January 1858, Lieutenant Nunes was shocked to see me so much shattered, and recommended me strongly to return at once to Tefé.

I took his advice, and embarked with him when he touched at São Paulo on his downward voyage, on the 2nd of February. I still hoped to be able to turn my face westward again to gather the yet unseen treasures of the marvelous countries lying between Sapurara and the slopes of the Andes, but although, after a short rest in Tefé, the ague left me, my general health remained in a state too weak to justify the undertaking of further journeys. At length I left Tefé, on the 3rd of February, 1859, en route for England.

BACK TO BELÉM

In rambling over my old ground in the forests of the neighborhood, I found great changes had taken place—to me, changes for the worse. The mantle of shrubs, bushes, and creeping plants which formerly, when the suburbs were undisturbed by ax or spade, had been left free to arrange itself in rich, full, and smooth sheets and masses over the forest borders, had been nearly all cut away, and troops of laborers were still employed cutting ugly muddy roads for carts and cattle through the once clean and lonely woods. Houses and mills had been erected on the borders of these new roads. The noble forest trees had been cut down, and their naked, half-burned stems remained in the midst of ashes, muddy puddles, and heaps of broken branches. I was obliged to hire a Negro boy to show me the way to my favorite path near Una . . . the new clearings having quite obliterated the old forest roads. Only a few acres of the glorious forest near Una now remained in their natural state.

On the other side of the city, near the old road to the rice mills, several scores of woodsmen were employed under the government in cutting a broad carriage road through the forest to São Luíz de Maranhão, the capital of the neighboring province, distant two hundred and fifty miles from Belém, and this had entirely destroyed the solitude of the grand old forest path. In the course of a few years, however, a new growth of creepers will cover the naked tree trunks on the borders of this new road and luxuriant shrubs form a green fringe to the path: it will then become as beautiful a woodland road as the old one was. A naturalist will have, henceforward, to go farther from the city to find the glorious forest scenery which lay so near in 1848, and work much more laboriously than was formerly needed to make the large collections which Mr. Wallace and I succeeded in doing in the neighborhood of Belém.

"A NATURALIST'S PARADISE"

The collections that I made during the whole eleven years were sent, at intervals of a few months, to London for distribution, except a set of species reserved for my own study, which remained with me and always accompanied me in my longer excursions. . . . The following is an approximate enumeration of the total number of species of the various classes which I obtained:

Mammals	52
Birds	360
Reptiles	140
Fishes	120
Insects	14,000
Mollusks	35
Zoophytes	5
	14,712

The part of the Amazon region where I resided longest being unexplored country to the naturalist, no less than eight thousand of the species here enumerated were *new to science*. . . .

part two

The Malay Archipelago

We stayed a day at desolate, volcanic Aden, and thence across to Galle, with its groves of cocoanut palms and crowds of natives offering for sale the precious stones of the country; thence across to Pulo Penang, with its picturesque mountain, its spice trees, and its waterfall, and on down the Straits of Malacca, with its richly wooded shores, to our destination, Singapore, where I was to begin the eight years of wandering throughout the Malay Archipelago, which constituted the central and controlling incident of my life.

WALLACE, *My Life*

7

A WORLD
OF ISLANDS

The Malay Archipelago extends for more
than 4,000 miles in length from east to
west, and is about 1,300 in breadth from
north to south.

WALLACE, *Malay Archipelago*

■ During the eight years from 1854 to 1862, Wallace
traveled fourteen thousand miles among the hundreds
of islands in this far corner of the earth. The islands
of this archipelago range in size from two of the
world's largest—Borneo and New Guinea—to tiny islets, and they cover an area almost as large as the
whole continent of South America. Most of them
contain mountains, many of which are volcanic, and
they are generally covered by tropical forests. But
though at first sight they may appear to be similar,
they are not simply larger or smaller copies of one another. Nor are they all even of the same age, for some
of them are much older than others.

Wallace had already discovered that the rivers of

South America formed the boundaries of the ranges of many animals. Here in this island world water was a still more obvious barrier, and many species of animals were confined to one or another of the islands. The opportunities for a collector were enormous, and Wallace plunged happily into his work.

The first two years were spent around Singapore and in Sarawak in northwest Borneo. By then Wallace felt he had served his apprenticeship and was ready for further exploration. His next goal was Makassar in Celebes, an island almost completely unknown to naturalists. But his travels in the archipelago depended on the available transportation, and he was forced to detour by way of two small volcanic islands, Bali and Lombok.

Bali is separated from the large island of Java by a strait that is only two miles wide at its narrowest point. Wallace was not surprised to find here many birds typical of Java. The distance to Lombok is not much greater, some twenty miles, but it was at this unexpected point that Wallace made one of his most startling discoveries—that this vast archipelago was not "one compact geographical whole" as had been thought. Instead, it is "divisible into two portions nearly equal in extent, which differ widely in their natural products and really form parts of two of the primary divisions of the earth."

The animals of the western islands resemble those of Asia, and the animals of the eastern islands resemble those of Australia; some of the middle islands have mixtures of representatives from both continents. In honor of his unexpected discovery, T. H. Huxley called this distributional boundary line "Wallace's Line," a

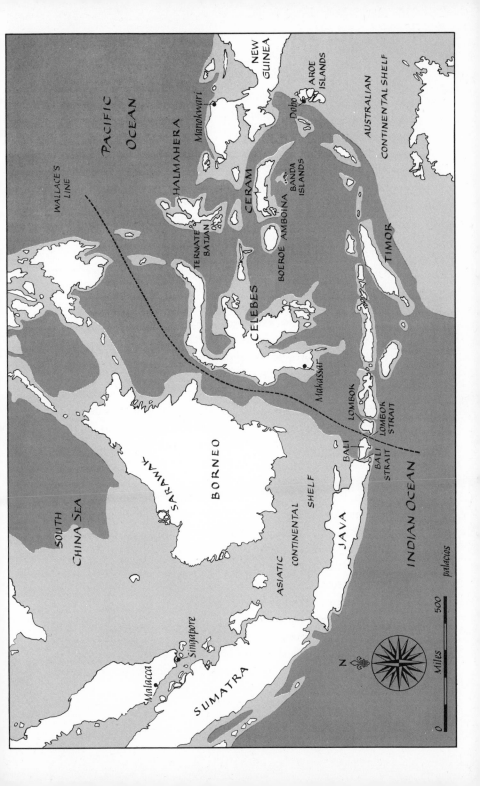

name that is still in use although variations of the line have since been proposed.

Perhaps the most surprising thing of all about this division is that the reason for it is hidden beneath the waters of the sea, invisible to the casual traveler. It is the depth of the sea itself. The seas on either side of the archipelago are shallow, covering the continental shelf; elsewhere the sea is much deeper. During the Pleistocene, or Ice Age, a great deal of water was removed from the sea by the formation of the glaciers. This lowered the sea level and laid bare the continental shelf. Islands on the continental shelves that are now separated by shallow seas were then connected by dry land and formed exposed parts of the continents of Asia and Australia. The melting of the glaciers caused a rise in the sea level and turned these regions into a multitude of islands. (Wallace suggested that "subsidence," or a sinking, of the earth's crust had brought this about. At the time he wrote, however, the study of glaciers and the Ice Age had barely begun.)

The narrow strait between Java and Bali is shallow and on the continental shelf, but the somewhat wider one between Bali and Lombok is not a part of the continental shelf and is much deeper. It would have remained as a water barrier even during times of lowered sea level. And water is often as much of a barrier to birds, in spite of their ability to fly, as it may be to other animals. Thus the birds that Wallace found on Lombok were different from those he had seen during his short stay on Bali.

Geologically speaking, this is an unstable part of the world, quite different from the long undisturbed forest region of the Amazon Valley. Not only have islands been made and unmade by changes in sea level, but many of them are also in a state of ferment through the action of volcanoes and earthquakes. Wallace never saw a volcanic eruption, but he did go through several earthquakes, the most severe one being in the northeast tip of Celebes.

But a still larger story lies behind the grand division of the archipelago into two parts and the many volcanoes and earthquakes that occur here, and that is the theory of continental drift. Wallace was convinced that the oceans and continents had always "maintained substantially the same positions." But in 1915 Alfred Wegener suggested that all continents were originally pieces of one large continent that have "drifted" to their present positions. Recent investigations have shown that at the present time North America and Europe are moving about an inch apart each year. On the other hand, according to this theory, Asia and Australia would once have been much farther apart than they are now and this would help to explain the differences in their animals.

After nearly four years of travel in the archipelago, Wallace set up his headquarters on the little volcanic island of Ternate, off the shore of the large Moluccan island of Halmahera. He had continued to mull over the problem he had set himself so long ago —how to explain the origin of species—and it was here, in February 1858, that the answer finally came to him. He had long since become convinced of evolution, of the gradual change in species through time, but how evolution worked had remained a mystery. Now at last he saw the solution, the theory of natural selection, and quickly writing out an outline of it, he sent it to his contemporary in England, Charles Darwin.

SINGAPORE

Few places are more interesting to a traveler from Europe than the town and island of Singapore. . . .

The island of Singapore consists of a multitude of small hills, three or four hundred feet high, the summits of many of which are still covered with virgin forest. The mission house at Bukit Timah [where the last remnant of original forest within forty miles of the city of Singapore can now be found] was surrounded by several of these wood-topped hills, which were much frequented by woodcutters and sawyers, and offered me an excellent collecting ground for insects. Here and there, too, were tiger pits, carefully covered over with sticks and leaves, and so well concealed that in several cases I had a narrow escape from falling into them. They are shaped like an iron furnace, wider at the bottom than the top, and are perhaps fifteen or twenty feet deep, so that it would be almost impossible for a person unassisted to get out of one. Formerly a sharp stake was stuck erect in the bottom; but after an unfortunate traveler had been killed by falling on one, its use was forbidden.

There are always a few tigers roaming about Singapore, and they kill on an average a Chinaman every day, principally those who work in the gambier plantations, which are always made in newly cleared jungle. We heard a tiger roar once or twice in the evening, and it was rather nervous work hunting for insects among the fallen trunks and old sawpits when one of these savage animals might be lurking close by, waiting an opportunity to spring upon us.

Several hours in the middle of every fine day were spent in these patches of forest, which were delightfully cool and shady by contrast with the bare open country we had to walk over to reach them. The vegetation was most luxuriant, comprising enormous forest trees as well as a variety of ferns, caladiums, and other undergrowth, and abundance of climbing rattan palms.

Insects were exceedingly abundant and very interesting, and every day furnished scores of new and curious forms. In about two months I obtained no less than 700 species of beetles, a large proportion of which were quite new, and among them were 130 distinct kinds of the elegant longicorns (Cerambycidae), so much esteemed by collectors. Almost all these were collected in one patch of jungle not more than a square mile in extent, and in all my subsequent travels in the East I rarely if ever met with so productive a spot.

This exceeding productiveness was due in part no doubt to some favorable conditions in the soil, climate, and vegetation, and to the season being very bright and sunny, with sufficient showers to keep everything fresh. But it was also in a great measure dependent, I feel sure, on the labors of the Chinese woodcutters. They had been at work here for several years, and during all that time had furnished a continual supply of dry and dead and decaying leaves and bark, together with abundance of wood and sawdust, for the nourishment of insects and their larvae. This had led to the assemblage of a great variety of species in a limited space, and I was the first natural-

ist who had come to reap the harvest they had prepared. In the same place, and during my walks in
other directions, I obtained a fair collection of butterflies and of other orders of insects, so that on the
whole I was quite satisfied with these my first at-
tempts to gain a knowledge of the natural history of
the Malay Archipelago.

JAVA

Taking it as a whole and surveying it from every
point of view, Java is probably the very finest and
most interesting tropical island in the world. It is not
first in size, but it is more than 600 miles long and
from 60 to 120 miles wide, and in area is nearly equal
to England; and it is undoubtedly the most fertile,
the most productive, and the most populous island
within the tropics.

Its whole surface is magnificently varied with
mountain and forest scenery. It possesses thirty-eight
volcanic mountains, several of which rise to ten or
twelve thousand feet high. Some of these are in constant activity, and one or other of them displays almost every phenomenon produced by the action of
subterranean fires, except regular lava streams, which
never occur in Java.

The abundant moisture and tropical heat of the
climate causes these mountains to be clothed with
luxuriant vegetation, often to their very summits,
while forests and plantations cover their lower slopes.
The animal productions, especially the birds and insects, are beautiful and varied, and present many pe-

culiar forms found nowhere else upon the globe. The
soil throughout the island is exceedingly fertile, and
all the productions of the tropics, together with many
of the temperate zones, can be easily cultivated.

Java too possesses a civilization, a history and an-
tiquities of its own, of great interest. The Brahmini-
cal religion flourished in it from an epoch of unknown antiquity till about the year 1478, when that
of Mahomet superseded it. The former religion was
accompanied by a civilization which has not been
equaled by the conquerors; for, scattered through the
country, especially in the eastern part of it, are found
buried in lofty forests, temples, tombs, and statues of
great beauty and grandeur; and the remains of extensive cities where the tiger, the rhinoceros, and the
wild bull now roam undisturbed.

WALLACE'S LINE

The islands of Bali and Lombok, situated at the
east end of Java, are particularly interesting. They are
the only islands of the whole archipelago in which
the Hindu religion still maintains itself—and they
form the extreme points of the two great zoological
divisions of the Eastern Hemisphere, for although so
similar in external appearance and in all physical features, they differ greatly in their natural productions.
It was after having spent two years in Borneo,
Malacca, and Singapore that I made a somewhat in-
voluntary visit to these islands on my way to Makassar. Had I been able to obtain a passage direct to that
place from Singapore, I should probably never have

gone near them, and should have missed some of the most important discoveries of my whole expedition to the East.

It was on the 13th of June, 1856, after twenty days' passage from Singapore in the *Kembang Dje-poon* (Rose of Japan), a schooner belonging to a Chinese merchant, manned by a Javanese crew and commanded by an English captain, that we cast anchor in the dangerous roadstead of Buleleng on the north side of the island of Bali. . . .

During the two days that we remained here, I walked out into the surrounding country to catch insects, shoot birds and spy out the nakedness or fertility of the land. I was both astonished and delighted, for as my visit to Java was some years later, I had never beheld so beautiful and well-cultivated a district out of Europe. . . . In so well-cultivated a country it was not to be expected that I could do much in natural history, and my ignorance of how important a locality this was for the elucidation of the geographical distribution of animals caused me to neglect obtaining some specimens which I never met with again.

One of these was a weaver bird with a bright yellow head, which built its bottle-shaped nests by dozens on some trees near the beach. It was the *Ploceus hypoxanthus,* a native of Java, and here at the extreme limits of its range westerly. I shot and preserved specimens of a wagtail thrush, an oriole, and some starlings, all species found in Java and some of them peculiar to that island. I also obtained some beautiful butterflies, richly marked with black and orange on a white ground, and which were the most abundant insects in the country lanes. Among them was a new species which I have named *Pieris tamar.*

Leaving Buleleng, a pleasant sail of two days brought us to Ampenan in the island of Lombok, where I proposed to remain till I could obtain a passage to Makassar. We enjoyed superb views of the twin volcanoes of Bali and Lombok, each about eight thousand feet high, which form magnificent objects at sunrise and sunset when they rise out of the mists and clouds that surround their bases, glowing with the rich and changing tints of these the most charm ing moments in a tropical day.

If we look at a map of the archipelago, nothing seems more unlikely than that the closely connected chain of islands from Java to Timor should differ materially in their natural productions. There are, it is true, certain differences of climate and of physical geography, but these do not correspond with the division the naturalist is obliged to make . . . the remarkable change in natural productions which occurs at the Strait of Lombok, separating the island of that name from Bali, and which is at once so large in amount and of so fundamental a character as to form an important feature in the zoological geography of our globe.

. . . During the few days which I stayed on the north coast of Bali on my way to Lombok, I saw several birds highly characteristic of Javan ornithology. Among these were the golden weaver (*Ploceus hypoxanthus*), the magpie robin (*Copsychus saularis*), the crimson-breasted barbet (*Megalaima haemacephala*), the black-naped oriole (*Oriolus chinensis*), the pied starling (*Sturnus contra*), and the goldenbacked three-toed woodpecker (*Dinopium javanese*).

On crossing over to Lombok, separated from Bali by a strait less than twenty miles wide, I naturally expected to meet with some of these birds again. But during a stay there of three months I never saw one of them, but found a totally different set of species, most of which were utterly unknown not only in Java, but also in Borneo, Sumatra, and Malacca. For example, among the commonest birds in Lombok were white cockatoos and three species of Meliphagidae, or honeyeaters, belonging to family groups which are entirely absent from the western or Indo-Malayan region of the archipelago. On passing to Flores and Timor the distinctness from the Javanese productions increases, and we find that these islands form a natural group whose birds are related to those of Java and Australia, but are quite distinct from either.

It was first pointed out . . . in 1845 . . . that a shallow sea connected the great islands of Sumatra, Java, and Borneo with the Asiatic continent, with which their natural productions generally agreed; while a similar shallow sea connected New Guinea and some of the islands adjacent to Australia, all being characterized by the presence of marsupials.

We have here a clue to the most radical contrast in the archipelago, and by following it out in detail I have arrived at the conclusion that we can draw a line among the islands which shall so divide them that one-half shall truly belong to Asia, while the other shall no less certainly be allied to Australia. I term these respectively the Indo-Malayan, and the Austro-Malayan divisions of the archipelago [or the Oriental and Australian regions].

EARTHQUAKE!

During my stay at Rurúkan [in northeastern Celebes] my curiosity was satisfied by experiencing a pretty sharp earthquake shock. On the evening of June 29th, at a quarter after eight, as I was sitting reading, the house began shaking with a very gentle but rapidly increasing motion. I sat still, enjoying the novel sensation for some seconds, but in less than half a minute it became strong enough to shake me in my chair and to make the house visibly rock about and creak and crack as if it would fall to pieces.

Then began a cry throughout the village of *"Tana goyang! tana goyang!"* (Earthquake! earthquake!). Everybody rushed out of their houses—women screamed and children cried—and I thought it prudent to go out too. On getting up, I found my head giddy and my steps unsteady, and could hardly walk without falling. The shock continued about a minute, during which time I felt as if I had been turned round and round and was almost seasick.

Going into the house again, I found a lamp and a bottle of arrack upset. The tumbler which formed the lamp had been thrown out of the saucer in which it had stood.

The shock appeared to be nearly vertical, rapid, vibratory, and jerking. It was sufficient, I have no doubt, to have thrown down brick chimneys and walls and church towers; but as the houses here are all low and strongly framed of timber, it is impossible for them to be much injured, except by a shock that would utterly destroy a European city. The people told me it was ten years since they had had a stronger shock than this, at which time many houses were thrown down and some people killed.

At intervals of ten minutes to half an hour, slight shocks and tremors were felt, sometimes strong enough to send us all out again. There was a strange mixture of the terrible and the ludicrous in our situation. We might at any moment have a much stronger shock, which would bring down the house over us, or—what I feared more—cause a landslip and send us down into the deep ravine on the very edge of which the village is built. Yet I could not help laughing each time we ran out at a slight shock, and then in a few moments ran in again. The sublime and the ridiculous were here literally but a step apart.

On the one hand, the most terrible and destructive of natural phenomena was in action around us— the rocks, the mountains, the solid earth were trembling and convulsed, and we were utterly impotent to guard against the danger that might at any moment overwhelm us.

On the other hand was the spectacle of a number of men, women, and children running in and out of their houses on what each time proved a very unnecessary alarm, as each shock ceased just as it became strong enough to frighten us. It seemed really very much like "playing at earthquakes," and made many of the people join me in a hearty laugh, even while reminding each other that it really might be no laughing matter.

At length the evening got very cold, and I became very sleepy and determined to turn in, leaving orders to my boys, who slept nearer the door, to wake me in case the house was in danger of falling. But I miscalculated my apathy, for I could not sleep much.

The shocks continued at intervals of half an hour or an hour all night, just strong enough to wake me thoroughly each time and keep me on the alert ready to jump up in case of danger. I was therefore very glad when morning came. Most of the inhabitants had not been to bed at all, and some had stayed out of doors all night.

For the next two days and nights shocks still continued at short intervals, and several times a day for a week, showing that there was some very extensive disturbance beneath our portion of the earth's crust.

How vast the forces at work really are can only be properly appreciated when, after feeling their effects, we look abroad over the wide expanse of hill and valley, plain and mountain, and thus realize in a slight degree the immense mass of matter heaved and shaken. The sensation produced by an earthquake is never to be forgotten. We feel ourselves in the grasp of a power to which the wildest fury of the winds and waves are as nothing; yet the effect is more a thrill of awe than the terror which the more boisterous war of the elements produces. There is a mystery and an uncertainty as to the amount of danger we incur which gives greater play to the imagination and to the influences of hope and fear. These remarks apply only to a moderate earthquake. A severe one is the most destructive and the most horrible catastrophe to which human beings can be exposed.

TERNATE

On the morning of the 8th of January, 1858, I arrived at Ternate, the fourth of a row of fine conical volcanic islands which skirt the west coast of the large and almost unknown island of Halmahera. The largest and most perfectly conical mountain is Tidore, which is over five thousand feet high—Ternate being very nearly the same height, but with a more rounded and irregular summit.

The town of Ternate is concealed from view till we enter between the two islands, when it is discovered stretching along the shore at the very base of the mountain. Its situation is fine, and there are grand views on every side.

Close opposite is the rugged promontory and beautiful volcanic cone of Tidore. To the east is the long mountainous coast of Halmahera, terminated toward the north by a group of three lofty volcanic peaks, while immediately behind the town rises the huge mountain, sloping easily at first and covered with thick groves of fruit trees, but soon becoming steeper and furrowed with deep gullies. Almost to the summit, whence issue perpetually faint wreaths of smoke, it is clothed with vegetation and looks calm and beautiful, although beneath are hidden fires which occasionally burst forth in lava streams, but more frequently make their existence known by the earthquakes which have many times devastated the town.

. . . I obtained a house, rather ruinous but well adapted to my purpose, being close to the town yet with a free outlet to the country and the mountain. A few needful repairs were soon made, some bamboo furniture and other necessaries obtained, and after a visit to the resident and police magistrate, I found myself an inhabitant of the earthquake-tortured island of Ternate, and able to look about me and lay down the plan of my campaign for the ensuing year.

I retained this house for three years, as I found it very convenient to have a place to return to after my voyages to the various islands of the Moluccas and New Guinea, where I could pack my collections, recruit my health, and make preparations for future journeys.

. . . The house is forty feet square, consists of four rooms, a hall, and two verandas, and is surrounded by a wilderness of fruit trees. A deep well supplied me with pure cold water, a great luxury in this climate. Five minutes' walk down the road brought me to the market and the beach, while in the opposite direction there were no more European houses between me and the mountain.

In this house I spent many happy days. Returning to it after a three or four months' absence in some uncivilized region, I enjoyed the unwonted luxuries of milk and fresh bread and regular supplies of fish and eggs, meat and vegetables, which were often sorely needed to restore my health and energy. I had ample space and convenience for unpacking, sorting, and arranging my treasures, and I had delightful walks in the suburbs of the town or up the lower slopes of the mountain, when I desired a little exercise or had time for collecting.

8

OBSERVATIONS
AND REFLECTIONS

But few European feet had ever trodden
the shores I gazed upon; its plants, and
animals, and men were alike almost unknown, and I could not help speculating on
what my wanderings there for a few days
might bring to light.

WALLACE, *Malay Archipelago*

■ Wallace was a collector, but more than that he was
an astute field observer, and he tried to understand
what he saw. His extensive travels gave him unrivaled
opportunities to see the products of nature in their
own surroundings, touched gently or not at all by
contact with man. The wild world of nature, after all,
arose independently of man, and travel in unfamiliar
wild places demonstrates this independence vividly.
As a stranger, one can easily see that this animal or
that plant has a life quite separate from one's own. In
fact, most of the life on this earth developed before
man appeared, and the adjustments and adaptations
of its different forms have, or had until comparatively
recently, little if anything to do with him.

160

One example that Wallace hoped to study was the orangutan, the huge but little known ape of Borneo and Sumatra. He wanted not only to collect specimens but also to learn something of its habits, for, as Thomas Huxley wrote shortly afterward, "Sound knowledge respecting the habits and mode of life of the man-like apes has been even more difficult of attainment than correct information regarding their structure."

Wallace's success can be measured by Huxley's praise:

Once in a generation, a Wallace may be found, physically, mentally, and morally qualified to wander unscathed through the tropical wilds of America and of Asia; to form magnificent collections as he wanders; and withal to think out sagaciously the conclusions suggested by his collections: but, to the ordinary explorer or collector, the dense forests of equatorial Asia and Africa, which constitute the favorite habitation of the orang, the chimpanzee, and the gorilla, present difficulties of no ordinary magnitude: and the man who risks his life by even a short visit to the malarious shores of those regions may well be excused if he shrinks from facing the dangers of the interior; if he contents himself with stimulating the industry of the better seasoned natives, and collecting and collating the more or less mythical reports and traditions with which they are too ready to supply him.

The orangutan might seem safe in such remote wildness, and yet, hardly more than a hundred years later, it is already threatened with extinction. Its habitat has been encroached upon and altered by man, and numbers of these animals have also been captured for exhibition in zoos. Only a few thousand now survive in the wild.

Another example of this independence is the fruit known as the durian. It is large and heavy and covered with stout spines, and when it falls from a great height, it may kill anyone struck by it. It is not, as Wallace notes, "organized with exclusive reference to the use and convenience of man." The spines, in fact, are a protection against its being eaten too soon, before the seeds are ripe.

How then could these adjustments, these delicate natural balances, have come about? They have been worked out over millions of years by the process of natural selection. Here the study of mimicry is helpful, for mimicry illustrates clearly how natural selection works. And because mimetic resemblances are only superficial and depend partly on the behavior of the live animal, it is field collectors like Wallace and Bates who are more likely to discover them. Bates discovered a number of mimetic butterflies in South America, and Wallace found more of them in the Malay Archipelago, some mimicking leaves and twigs and others mimicking other butterflies. Even more remarkable were two rare cases of Batesian mimicry in birds.

Such examples show that the natural forces producing them have operated entirely independently of man either as manipulator or intermediary, or even as beneficiary. Man is but one part, and a recent one at that, of the whole natural system. He may now be in a position to interfere with it, but he is not exempt

from its laws, and this makes it all the more important that he understand them.

ORANGUTANS

One of my chief objects in coming to stay at
Simanggang was to see the orangutan (or great man-
like ape of Borneo) in his native haunts, to study his
habits, and obtain good specimens of the different varieties and species of both sexes and of the adult and
young animals. In all these objects I succeeded beyond my expectations. . . .

The orangutan is known to inhabit Sumatra and
Borneo, and there is every reason to believe that it is
confined to these two great islands, in the former of
which, however, it seems to be much more rare. In
Borneo it has a wide range, inhabiting many districts
on the southwest, southeast, northeast, and northwest
coasts, but appears to be chiefly confined to the low
and swampy forests. . . .

Now it seems to me probable that a wide extent
of unbroken and equally lofty virgin forest is necessary
to the comfortable existence of these animals. Such
forests form their open country, where they can roam
in every direction with as much facility as the Indian
on the prairie or the Arab on the desert, passing from
treetop to treetop without ever being obliged to descend upon the earth. . . .

It is a singular and very interesting sight to
watch a *mias* [the native name for the orangutan]
making his way leisurely through the forest. He walks
deliberately along some of the larger branches in the
semierect attitude which the great length of his arms

and the shortness of his legs cause him naturally to assume; and the disproportion between these limbs is increased by his walking on his knuckles, not on the palm of the hand as we should do.

He seems always to choose those branches which intermingle with an adjoining tree, on approaching which he stretches out his long arms, and seizing the opposing boughs, grasps them together with both hands, seems to try their strength, and then deliberately swings himself across to the next branch, on which he walks along as before. He never jumps or springs, or even appears to hurry himself, and yet manages to get along almost as quickly as a person can run through the forest beneath.

The long and powerful arms are of the greatest use to the animal, enabling it to climb easily up the loftiest trees, to seize fruits and young leaves from slender boughs which will not bear its weight, and to gather leaves and branches with which to form its nest . . . [which] it uses to sleep on almost every night. This is placed low down, however, on a small tree not more than from twenty to fifty feet from the ground, probably because it is warmer and less exposed to wind than higher up. . . . The Dyaks [an aboriginal tribe of Borneo] say that when it is very wet, the mias covers himself over with leaves of pandanus, or large ferns, which has perhaps led to the story of his making a hut in the trees.

The orang does not leave his bed till the sun has well risen and has dried up the dew upon the leaves. He feeds all through the middle of the day, but seldom returns to the same tree two days running. . . . Their food consists almost exclusively of fruit, with occasionally leaves, buds, and young shoots.

They seem to prefer unripe fruits, some of which were very sour, others intensely bitter. . . . In other cases they eat only the small seed of a large fruit, and they almost always waste and destroy more than they eat, so that there is a continual rain of rejected portions below the tree they are feeding on.

The durian is an especial favorite, and quantities of this delicious fruit are destroyed wherever it grows surrounded by forest, but they will not cross clearings to get at them. It seems wonderful how the animal can tear open this fruit, the outer covering of which is so thick and tough and closely covered with strong conical spines. It probably bites off a few of these first, and then, making a small hole, tears open the fruit with its powerful fingers.

The mias rarely descends to the ground, except when pressed by hunger it seeks for succulent shoots by the river side, or in very dry weather has to search after water, of which it generally finds sufficient in the hollows of leaves. . . .

The Dyaks all declare that the mias is never attacked by any animal in the forest, with two rare exceptions; and the accounts I received of these are so curious that I give them nearly in the words of my informants, old Dyak chiefs, who had lived all their lives in the places where the animal is most abundant.

The first of whom I inquired said: "No animal is strong enough to hurt the mias, and the only creature he ever fights with is the crocodile. When there is no fruit in the jungle, he goes to seek food on the banks of the river, where there are plenty of young shoots that he likes and fruits that grow close to the water. Then the crocodile sometimes tries to seize him, but the mias gets upon him, and beats him with his hands and feet, and tears him and kills him." He added that he had once seen such a fight, and that he believes that the mias is always the victor.

My next informant was the *orang kaya,* or chief of the Balow Dyaks, on the Simaggang River. He said: "The mias has no enemies; no animals dare attack it but the crocodile and the python. He always kills the crocodile by main strength, standing upon it, pulling open its jaws and ripping up its throat. If a python attacks a mias, he seizes it with his hands and then bites it, and soon kills it. The mias is very strong; there is no animal in the jungle so strong as he."

It is very remarkable that an animal so large, so peculiar, and of such a high type of form as the orangutan, should be confined to so limited a district—to two islands, and those almost the last inhabited by the higher Mammalia . . . [which] eastward of Borneo and Java . . . diminish rapidly, and soon entirely disappear.

When we consider further that almost all other animals have in earlier ages been represented by allied yet distinct forms—that in the latter part of the Tertiary period Europe was inhabited by bears, deer, wolves, and cats; Australia by kangaroos and other marsupials; South America by gigantic sloths and anteaters; all different from any now existing, though intimately allied to them—we have every reason to believe that the orangutan, the chimpanzee, and the gorilla have also had their forerunners. With what interest must every naturalist look forward to the time when the caves and Tertiary deposits of the tropics may be thoroughly examined, and the past history and earliest appearance of the great manlike apes be at length known.

. . . while preparing to carry [a dead female mias] home, we found a young one face downward in the bog. This little creature was only about a foot long, and had evidently been hanging to its mother when she first fell. Luckily it did not appear to have been wounded, and after we had cleaned the mud out of its mouth, it began to cry out and seemed quite strong and active. While carrying it home it got its hands in my beard and grasped so tightly that I had great difficulty in getting free, for the fingers are habitually bent inward at the last joint so as to form complete hooks.

At this time it had not a single tooth, but a few days afterward it cut its two lower front teeth. Unfortunately I had no milk to give it, as neither Malays, Chinese, nor Dyaks ever use the article, and I in vain inquired for any female animal that could suckle my little infant. I was therefore obliged to give it rice-water from a bottle with a quill in the cork, which after a few trials it learned to suck very well. This was very meager diet, and the little creature did not thrive well on it, although I added sugar and cocoanut milk occasionally to make it more nourishing. . . .

After the first week I found I could feed it better with a spoon and give it a little more varied and more solid food. Well-soaked biscuit mixed with a little egg and sugar, and sometimes sweet potatoes, were readily eaten, and it was a never-failing amusement to observe the curious changes of countenance by which it would express its approval or dislike of what was given to it.

The poor little thing would lick its lips, draw in its cheeks, and turn up its eyes with an expression of the most supreme satisfaction when it had a mouthful particularly to its taste. On the other hand, when its food was not sufficiently sweet or palatable, it would turn the mouthful about with its tongue for a moment as if trying to extract what flavor there was, and then push it all out between its lips. If the same food was continued, it would set up a scream and kick violently, exactly like a baby in a passion.

After I had had the little mias about three weeks, I fortunately obtained a young monkey, a crab-eating macaque (*Macaca irus*), which, though small, was very active and could feed itself. I placed it in the same box with the mias and they immediately became excellent friends, neither exhibiting the least fear of the other. The little monkey would sit upon the other's stomach, or even on its face, without the least regard to its feelings.

While I was feeding the mias, the monkey would sit by, picking up all that was spilled and occasionally putting out its hands to intercept the spoon; and as soon as I had finished would pick off what was left sticking to the mias' lips and then pull open its mouth and see if any still remained inside; afterward lying down on the poor creature's stomach as on a comfortable cushion. The little helpless mias would submit to all these insults with the most exemplary patience, only too glad to have something warm near it which it could clasp affectionately in its arms. It sometimes, however, had its revenge; for when the monkey wanted to go away, the mias would hold on as long as it could by the loose skin of its back or head, or by its tail, and it was only after many vigorous jumps that the monkey could make his escape.

It was curious to observe the different actions of these two animals, which could not have differed much in age. The mias, like a very young baby, lying on its back quite helpless, rolling lazily from side to side, stretching out all four hands into the air, wishing to grasp something but hardly able to guide its fingers to any definite object and when dissatisfied, opening wide its almost toothless mouth and expressing its wants by a most infantine scream. The little monkey, on the other hand, in constant motion: running and jumping about wherever it pleased, examining everything around it, seizing hold of the smallest objects with the greatest precision, balancing itself on the edge of the box or running up a post, and helping itself to anything eatable that came in its way. There could hardly be a greater contrast, and the baby mias looked more babylike by the comparison. . . .

After five weeks it cut its two upper front teeth, but in all this time it had not grown the least bit, remaining both in size and weight the same as when I first procured it. This was no doubt owing to the want of milk or other equally nourishing food. Rice-water, rice, and biscuits were but a poor substitute, and the expressed milk of the cocoanut which I sometimes gave it did not quite agree with its stomach. To this I imputed an attack of diarrhea from which the poor little creature suffered greatly, but a small dose of castor oil operated well and cured it.

A week or two afterward it was again taken ill, and this time more seriously. The symptoms were exactly those of intermittent fever, accompanied by watery swellings on the feet and head. It lost all appetite for its food, and after lingering for a week a most pitiable object, died, after being in my possession nearly three months.

I much regretted the loss of my little pet, which I had at one time looked forward to bringing up to years of maturity and taking home to England. For several months it had afforded me daily amusement by its curious ways and the inimitably ludicrous expression of its little countenance. Its weight was three pounds nine ounces, its height fourteen inches, and the spread of its arms twenty-three inches. I preserved its skin and skeleton, and in doing so found that when it fell from the tree it must have broken an arm and a leg, which had, however, united so rapidly that I had only noticed the hard swellings on the limbs where the irregular junction of the bones had taken place.

THE DURIAN

Many persons in Europe are under the impression that fruits of delicious flavor abound in the tropical forests, and they will no doubt be surprised to learn that the truly wild fruits of this grand and luxuriant archipelago, the vegetation of which will vie with that of any part of the world, are in almost every island inferior in abundance and quality to those of Britain.

Wild strawberries and raspberries are found in some places, but they are such poor tasteless things as to be hardly worth eating, and there is nothing to compare with our blackberries and whortleberries.

The kanarynut [an edible East Indian nut] may be considered equal to a hazelnut, but I have met with nothing else superior to our crabs, our haws, beechnuts, wild plums, and acorns—fruits which would be highly esteemed by the natives of these islands and would form an important part of their sustenance. All the fine tropical fruits are as much cultivated productions as our apples, peaches, and plums, and their wild prototypes, when found, are generally either tasteless or uneatable.

. . . but most abundant and most esteemed is the durian, a fruit about which very little is known in England, but which both by natives and Europeans in the Malay Archipelago is reckoned superior to all others. . . . When brought into a house the smell is often so offensive that some persons can never bear to taste it. This was my own case when I first tried it in Malacca, but in Borneo I found a ripe fruit on the ground, and eating it out of doors, I at once became a confirmed durian eater.

The durian grows on a large and lofty forest tree, somewhat resembling an elm in its general character, but with a more smooth and scaly bark. The fruit is round or slightly oval, about the size of a large cocoanut, of a green color, and covered all over with short stout spines, the bases of which touch each other and are consequently somewhat hexagonal, while the points are very strong and sharp. It is so completely armed that if the stalk is broken off, it is a difficult matter to lift one from the ground. The outer rind is so thick and tough that from whatever height it may fall it is never broken. From the base to the apex five very faint lines may be traced, over which the spines

171

arch a little; these are the sutures of the carpels, and show where the fruit may be divided with a heavy knife and a strong hand. The five cells are satiny white within, and are each filled with an oval mass of cream-colored pulp, imbedded in which are two or three seeds about the size of chestnuts.

This pulp is the eatable part, and its consistence and flavor are indescribable. A rich butterlike custard highly flavored with almonds gives the best general idea of it, but intermingled with it come wafts of flavor that call to mind cream cheese, onion sauce, brown sherry, and other incongruities. Then there is a rich glutinous smoothness in the pulp which nothing else possesses, but which adds to its delicacy. It is neither acid nor sweet nor juicy, yet one feels the want of none of these qualities, for it is perfect as it is. It produces no nausea or other bad effect, and the more you eat of it the less you feel inclined to stop. In fact, to eat durians is a new sensation, worth a voyage to the East to experience.

When the fruit is ripe it falls of itself, and the only way to eat durians in perfection is to get them as they fall, and the smell is then less overpowering. When unripe, it makes a very good vegetable if cooked, and it is also eaten by the Dyaks raw. In a good fruit season large quantities are preserved salted, in jars and bamboos, and kept the year round, when it acquiries a most disgusting odor to Europeans, but the Dyaks appreciate it highly as a relish with their rice.

There are in the forest two varieties of wild durians with much smaller fruits, one of them orange-colored inside, and these are probably the origin of the large and fine durians, which are never found wild. It would not, perhaps, be correct to say that the durian is the best of all fruits, because it cannot supply the place of the subacid juicy kinds such as the orange, grape, mango, and mangosteen, whose refreshing and cooling qualities are so wholesome and grateful; but as producing a food of the most exquisite flavor it is unsurpassed. If I had to fix on two only as representing the perfection of the two classes, I should certainly choose the durian and the orange as the king and queen of fruits.

The durian is, however, sometimes dangerous. When the fruit begins to ripen it falls daily and almost hourly, and accidents not unfrequently happen to persons walking or working under the trees. When a Durian strikes a man in its fall, it produces a dreadful wound, the strong spines tearing open the flesh, while the blow itself is very heavy. But from this very circumstance death rarely ensues, the copious effusion of blood preventing the inflammation which might otherwise take place. . . .

Poets and moralists, judging from our English trees and fruits, have thought that small fruits always grew on lofty trees, so that their fall should be harmless to man, while the large ones trailed on the ground. Two of the largest and heaviest fruits known, however, the Brazil nut fruit (*Bertholletia*) and the durian, grow on lofty forest trees, from which they fall as soon as they are ripe, and often wound or kill the native inhabitants.

From this we may learn two things: first, not to draw general conclusions from a very partial view of nature; and secondly, that trees and fruits, no less than the varied productions of the animal kingdom, do not appear to be organized with exclusive reference to the use and convenience of man.

MIMETIC BUTTERFLIES

Lubukraman is a central point of the east end of Sumatra. . . . During a month's collecting I added only three or four new species to my list of birds, although I obtained very fine specimens of many which were rare and interesting. In butterflies I was rather more successful, obtaining several fine species quite new to me, and a considerable number of very rare and beautiful insects. I will give here some account of two species of butterflies which, though very common in collections, present us with peculiarities of the highest interest.

The first is the handsome *Papilio memnon*, a splendid butterfly of a deep black color, dotted over with lines and groups of scales of a clear ashy-blue. Its wings are five inches in expanse and the hind wings are rounded, with scalloped edges. This applies to the males; but the females are very different, and vary so much that they were once supposed to form several distinct species.

They may be divided into two groups—those which resemble the male in shape and those which differ entirely from him in the outline of the wings. The first vary much in color, being often nearly white with dusky yellow and red markings, but such differences often occur in butterflies.

The second group are much more extraordinary, and would never be supposed to be the same insect, since the hind wings are lengthened out into large spoon-shaped tails, no rudiment of which is ever to be perceived in the males or in the ordinary form of females. These tailed females are never of the dark and blue-glossed tints which prevail in the male and often occur in the females of the same form, but are invariably ornamented with stripes and patches of white or buff, occupying the larger part of the surface of the hind wings. This peculiarity of coloring led me to discover that this extradordinary female closely resembles (when flying) another butterfly of the same genus but of a different group (*Papilio coon*), and that we have here a case of mimicry similar to those so well illustrated and explained by Mr. Bates. . . .

The use and reason of this resemblance appears to be that the butterflies imitated belong to a section of the genus *Papilio* which from some cause or other are not attacked by birds, and by so closely resembling these in form and color the female of *memnon* and its ally also escape persecution. . . .

The other species to which I have to direct attention is the *Kallima paralekta,* a butterfly of the same family group as our purple emperor and of about the same size or larger. Its upper surface is of a rich purple variously tinged with ash color, and across the fore wings there is a broad bar of deep orange, so that when on the wing it is very conspicuous.

This species was not uncommon in dry woods and thickets, and I often endeavor to capture it without success, for after flying a short distance it would enter a bush among dry or dead leaves, and however carefully I crept up to the spot I could never discover it till it would suddenly start out again and then disappear in a similar place.

At length I was fortunate enough to see the exact spot where the butterfly settled, and though I lost sight of it for some time, I at length discovered that it was close before my eyes, but that in its position of repose it so closely resembled a dead leaf attached to a twig as almost certainly to deceive the eye even when gazing full upon it. I captured several specimens on the wing, and was able fully to understand the way in which this wonderful resemblance is produced.

The end of the upper wings terminates in a fine point, just as the leaves of many tropical shrubs and trees are pointed, while the lower wings are somewhat more obtuse and are lengthened out into a short thick tail. Between these two points there runs a dark curved line exactly representing the midrib of a leaf, and from this radiate on each side a few oblique marks which well imitate the lateral veins. These marks are more clearly seen on the outer portion of the base of the wings and on the inner side toward the middle and apex, and they are produced by striae and markings which are very common in allied species, but which are here modified and strengthened so as to imitate more exactly the venation of a leaf. The tint of the under surface varies much, but it is always some ashy-brown or reddish color, which matches with those of dead leaves.

The habit of the species is always to rest on a twig and among dead or dry leaves, and in this position, with the wings closely pressed together, their outline is exactly that of a moderately sized leaf slightly curled or shriveled. The tail of the hind wings forms a perfect stalk and touches the stick, while the insect is supported by the middle pair of legs, which are not noticed among the twigs and fibers that surround it. The head and antennae are drawn back between the wings so as to be quite concealed, and there is a little notch hollowed out at the very base of the wings which allows the head to be retracted sufficiently.

All these varied details combine to produce a disguise that is so complete and marvelous as to astonish every one who observes it; and the habits of the insects are such as to utilize all these peculiarities and render them available in such a manner as to remove all doubt of the purpose of this singular case of mimicry, which is undoubtedly a protection to the insect. Its strong and swift flight is sufficient to save it from its enemies when on the wing, but if it were equally conspicuous when at rest it could not long escape extinction, owing to the attacks of the insectivorous birds and reptiles that abound in the tropical forests. . . .

If such an extraordinary adaptation as this stood alone, it would be very difficult to offer any explanation of it; but although it is perhaps the most perfect case of protective imitation known, there are hundreds of similar resemblances in nature, and from these it is possible to deduce a general theory of the manner in which they have been slowly brought about. The principal of variation and that of "natural selection" . . . offers the foundation for such a theory. . . .

MIMETIC BIRDS

It was in the Moluccas that I first discovered undoubted cases of "mimicry" among birds, and these are so curious that I must briefly describe them. It will

177

be as well, however, first to explain what is meant by mimicry in natural history. . . . I have described a butterfly which, when at rest, so closely resembles a dead leaf that it thereby escapes the attacks of its enemies. This is termed a "protective resemblance."

If, however, the butterfly, being itself a savory morsel to birds, had closely resembled another butterfly which was disagreeable to birds and therefore never eaten by them, it would be as well protected as if it resembled a leaf; and this is what has been happily termed mimicry by Mr. Bates, who first discovered the object of these curious external imitations of one insect by another belonging to a distinct genus or family, and sometimes even to a distinct order. . . .

For a long time all the known cases of exact resemblance of one creature to quite a different one were confined to insects, and it was therefore with great pleasure that I discovered in the island of Boeroe two birds which I constantly mistook for each other and which yet belonged to two distinct and somewhat distant families. One of these is a honeyeater named *Philemon bouroensis,* and the other a kind of oriole which has been called *Oriolus bouroensis.*

The oriole resembles the honeyeater in the following particulars: the upper and under surfaces of the two birds are exactly of the same tints of dark and light brown; the honeyeater [a friar bird] has a large bare black patch round the eyes; this is copied in the oriole by a patch of black feathers. The top of the head of the honeyeater has a scaly appearance from the narrow scale-formed feathers, which are imitated by the broader feathers of the oriole having a dusky line down each.

The honeyeater has a pale ruff formed of curious recurved feathers on the nape (which has given the whole genus the name of friar birds) ; this is represented in the oriole by a pale band in the same position. Lastly, the bill of the honeyeater is raised into a protuberant keel at the base, and the oriole has the same character, although it is not a common one in the genus. The result is that on a superficial examination the birds are identical, although they have important structural differences and cannot be placed near each other in any natural arrangement.

In the adjacent island of Ceram we find very distinct species of both these genera, and, strange to say, these resemble each other quite as closely as do those of Boeroe. The *Philemon subcornutus* is of an earthy-brown color washed with ocherish yellow, with bare orbits, dusky cheeks, and the usual recurved nape ruff. The *Oriolus forsteni* which accompanies it is absolutely identical in the tints of every part of the body, and the details are copied just as minutely as in the former species.

We have two kinds of evidence to tell us which bird in this case is the model and which the copy. The honeyeaters are colored in a manner which is very general in the whole family to which they belong, while the orioles seem to have departed from the gay yellow tints so common among their allies. We should therefore conclude that it is the latter who mimic the former. If so, however, they must derive some advantage from the imitation, and as they are certainly weak birds, with small feet and claws, they may require it.

Now the friar birds are very strong and active birds, having powerful grasping claws and long, curved, sharp beaks. They assemble together in groups and small flocks, and they have a very loud bawling note which can be heard at a great distance. They are very plentiful and very pugnacious, frequently driving away crows and even hawks, which perch on a tree where a few of them are assembled.

It is very probable, therefore, that the smaller birds of prey have learned to respect these birds and leave them alone, and it may thus be a great advantage for the weaker and less courageous orioles to be mistaken for them. This being the case, the laws of variation and survival of the fittest will suffice to explain how the resemblance has been brought about, without supposing any voluntary action on the part of the birds themselves. . . .

9

BIRDS
OF PARADISE

I looked with intense interest on those rugged mountains, retreating ridge behind ridge into the interior, where the foot of civilized man had never trod. There was the country of the cassowary and the tree kangaroo, and those dark forests produced the most extraordinary and the most beautiful of the feathered inhabitants of the earth— the varied species of birds of paradise.

WALLACE, *Malay Archipelago*

■The rewards, the dangers, and the difficulties of Wallace's adventures among the islands of the Malay Archipelago are summed up in his experiences with the birds of paradise.

These strange and beautiful birds are found only in the eastern part of the archipelago. Their principal home is New Guinea, but they also occur on neighboring islands and in Australia. Their distribution, like Wallace's Line, is related to the continental shelf, for the islands on which they live would have been a single land mass during the Pleistocene, when the sea level was lower (see map on page 145). With one exception, the birds of paradise have not spread beyond this area. The exception was one of Wallace's more

181

exciting discoveries, a previously unknown species living on the Moluccan islands of Batjan and Halmahera. These islands are separated from New Guinea by deeper seas, as Lombok is from Bali. Perhaps the winds of the southeast monsoon, blowing from the southeast to the northwest nine months of the year, blew ancestors of the present species across the intervening water.

The scientific name of the largest species, the greater bird of paradise, is *Paradisaea apoda*. Apoda means "without feet," and this unusual name gives an inkling of the mystery that surrounded these birds. Of course there are no birds without feet. But most birds of paradise live in extremely remote areas in New Guinea that even today are almost inaccessible; in fact, more than half of the presently known species were discovered after Wallace's travels. Perhaps partly because they were so difficult to obtain, they became valuable articles of trade and tribute. Natives caught and killed the birds and then preserved them, part of the procedure being to cut off their feet. Naturally the first specimens to reach Europe were footless, and this bit of history is recorded in the scientific name.

As with the orangutan, Wallace hoped also to learn something about the habits of these wonderful birds. It is an indication of the sparseness of such information that some of his observations on the greater bird of paradise have only recently been confirmed, a hundred years later. In 1909 this bird was introduced into a small island in the West Indies, where it has since flourished. Wallace described the actions of a group of the birds displaying their gorgeous feathers, and this has at last been photographed.

The search for the elusive birds of paradise took Wallace on some of his most daring and dangerous journeys—to the Aroe Islands, to New Guinea and to Waigeo. As Darwin wrote to him later, "that you ever returned alive is wonderful after all your risks from illness and sea voyages . . . your perseverance in the cause of science was heroic."

During his eight years of travel, Wallace met with nearly every kind of adventure imaginable, but he kept going in spite of countless difficulties. He hoped this time to assure himself of sufficient money so that he would not have to return to surveying, and he was absorbed in making scientific observations. From every point of view his efforts were rewarded with success. He was well repaid for the grand total of 125,000 specimens that he collected (although the caution against such large-scale collecting in these very different times should be repeated). Furthermore, his original scientific contributions put him in the front rank of English scientists.

But he eventually began to tire of the stupendous effort. The repeated preparations, the constant travel ("some sixty or seventy separate journeys"), the growing familiarity with what at first had seemed so novel: all began to take their toll, and he finally complained in a letter to Bates of his "too monotonous existence"!

And so he turned his steps toward home, returning by way of Timor and Boeroe to Makassar in Celebes, and thence to Java and Sumatra and back to Singapore. But still his irrepressible self, his eye was attracted by some live birds for sale in Singapore. He bought them and successfully transported them back to England.

BIRDS WITHOUT FEET

As many of my journeys were made with the express object of obtaining specimens of the birds of paradise and learning something of their habits and distribution, and being (as far as I am aware) the only Englishman who has seen these wonderful birds in their native forests and obtained specimens of many of them, I propose to give here . . . the result of my observations and inquiries.

When the earliest European voyagers reached the Moluccas in search of cloves and nutmegs, which were then rare and precious spices, they were presented with the dried skins of birds so strange and beautiful as to excite the admiration even of those wealth-seeking rovers. The Malay traders gave them the name of *manuk dewata,* or God's birds; and the Portuguese, finding that they had no feet or wings, and not being able to learn anything authentic about them, called them *passaros de sol,* or birds of the sun; while the learned Dutchmen, who wrote in Latin, called them *avis paradiseus,* or paradise bird.

Jan van Linschoten [an early Dutch traveler] gives these names in 1598 and tells us that no one has seen these birds alive, for they live in the air, always turning toward the sun and never lighting on the earth till they die; for they have neither feet nor wings, as, he adds, may be seen by the birds carried to India and sometimes to Holland, but being very costly they were then rarely seen in Europe. More than a hundred years later Mr. William Funnel, who accompanied [William] Dampier [on his travels in the Far East], and wrote an account of the voyage, saw specimens at Amboina, and was told that they came to Banda to eat nutmegs, which intoxicated them and made them fall down senseless, when they were killed by ants.

Down to 1760, when Linnaeus named the largest species *Paradisaea apoda* (the footless paradise bird), nothing was known about them. And even now, a hundred years later, most books state that they migrate annually to Ternate, Banda, and Amboina; whereas the fact is that they are as completely unknown in those islands in a wild state as they are in England.

Linnaeus was also acquainted with a small species, which he named *Paradisaea regio* (the king bird of paradise), and since then nine or ten others have been named, all of which were first described from skins preserved by the savages of New Guinea, and generally more or less imperfect. These are now all known in the Malay Archipelago as *burong mati*, or dead birds, indicating that the Malay traders never saw them alive.

The Paradisaeidae are a group of moderate-sized birds, allied in their structure and habits to crows, starlings, and to the Australian honeyeaters, but they are characterized by extraordinary developments of plumage which are unequaled in any other family of birds. In several species large tufts of delicate bright-colored feathers spring from each side of the body beneath the wings, forming trains or fans or shields;

and the middle feathers of the tail are often elongated into wires, twisted into fantastic shapes, or adorned with the most brilliant metallic tints.

In another set of species these accessory plumes spring from the head, the back, or the shoulders, while the intensity of color and of metallic luster displayed by their plumage is not to be equaled by any other birds except, perhaps, the hummingbirds, and is not surpassed even by these. . . .

Although I devoted so much time to a search after these wonderful birds, I only succeeded myself in obtaining five species during a residence of many months in the Aroe Islands, New Guinea, and Waigeo. . . . it is necessary to consider that the birds of paradise are an article of commerce and are the monopoly of the chiefs of the coast villages, who obtain them at a low rate from the mountaineers and sell them to . . . traders. . . . Five voyages to different parts of the district they inhabit, each occupying in its preparation and execution the larger part of a year, produced me only five species out of the fourteen known to exist in the New Guinea district. The kinds obtained are those that inhabit the coasts of New Guinea and its islands, the remainder seeming to be strictly confined to the central mountain ranges of the northern peninsula. . . .

The trade to [the Aroe] islands has existed from very early times, and it is from them that birds of paradise of the two kinds known to Linnaeus were first brought. The native vessels can only make the voyage once a year, owing to the monsoons. They leave Makassar [in southern Celebes] in December or January at the beginning of the west monsoon, and return in July or August with the full strength of the east monsoon.

Even by the Makassar people themselves, the voyage to the Aroe Islands is looked upon as a rather wild and romantic expedition, full of novel sights and strange adventures. He who has made it is looked up to as an authority, and it remains with many the unachieved ambition of their lives. I myself had hoped rather than expected ever to reach this "ultima Thule" of the East. And when I found that I really could do so now—had I but courage to trust myself for a thousand miles' voyage in a Bugis prau and for six or seven months among lawless traders and ferocious savages—I felt somewhat as I did when, a schoolboy, I was for the first time allowed to travel outside the stagecoach, to visit that scene of all that is strange and new and wonderful to young imaginations—London!

By the help of some kind friends I was introduced to the owner of one of the large praus which was to sail in a few days. . . . It was a vessel of about seventy tons' burthen and shaped something like a Chinese junk. . . . The crew consisted of about thirty men, natives of Makassar and the adjacent coasts and islands. . . .

On the 8th of January, 1857, I landed at Dobo, the trading settlement of the Bugis and Chinese, who annually visit the Aroe Islands. It is situated on the small island of Wamar, upon a spit of sand which projects out to the north and is just wide enough to contain three rows of houses. . . .

Before leaving Makassar, I had written to the governor of Amboina requesting him to assist me with the native chiefs of Aroe. I now received by a vessel which had arrived from Amboina a very polite answer, informing me that orders had been sent to give me every assistance that I might require; and I was just congratulating myself on being at length able to get a boat and men to go to the mainland and explore the interior when a sudden check came in the form of a piratical incursion.

A small prau arrived which had been attacked by pirates and had a man wounded. They were said to have five boats, but more were expected to be behind, and the traders were all in consternation, fearing that their small vessels sent trading to the *blakang tana* [the other side of the islands] would be plundered. The Aroe natives were of course dreadfully alarmed, as these marauders attack their villages, burn and murder, and carry away women and children for slaves. Not a man will stir from his village for some time, and I must remain still a prisoner in Dobo. The governor of Amboina, out of pure kindness, has told the chiefs that they are to be responsible for my safety, so that they have an excellent excuse for refusing to stir.

Several praus went out in search of the pirates, sentinels were appointed, and watch fires lighted on the beach to guard against the possibility of a night attack, though it was hardly thought they would be bold enough to plunder Dobo. The next day the praus returned and we had positive information that these scourges of the eastern seas were really among us. . . . They are said to be Sulu pirates, but have Bugis [also formerly notorious as pirates] among them. On their way here they have devastated one of the small islands east of Ceram.

It is now eleven years since they have visited

Aroe, and by thus making their attacks at long and uncertain intervals, the alarm dies away and they find a population for the most part unarmed and unsuspicious of danger. None of the small trading vessels now carry arms, though they did so for a year or two after the last attack, which was just the time when there was the least occasion for it.

A week later one of the smaller pirate boats was captured in the blakang tana. Seven men were killed and three taken prisoners. The larger vessels have been often seen but cannot be caught, as they have very strong crews and can always escape by rowing out to sea in the eye of the wind, returning at night. They will thus remain among the innumerable islands and channels till the change of the monsoon enables them to sail westward. . . .

My boat was at length ready, and having obtained two men besides my own servants, after an enormous amount of talk and trouble we left Dobo on the morning of March 13th for the mainland of Aroe. . . .

The first two or three days of our stay here were very wet and I obtained but few insects or birds, but at length when I was beginning to despair, my boy Baderoon returned one day with a specimen which repaid me for months of delay and expectation.

It was a small bird, a little less than a thrush. The greater part of its plumage was of an intense cinnabar red, with a gloss as of spun glass. On the head the feathers became short and velvety and shaded into rich orange. Beneath, from the breast downward, was pure white, with the softness and gloss of silk, and across the breast a band of deep metallic green separated this color from the red of the throat. Above each eye was a round spot of the same metallic green; the bill was yellow, and the feet and legs were of a fine cobalt blue, strikingly contrasting with all the other parts of the body.

Merely in arrangement of colors and texture of plumage this little bird was a gem of the first water; yet these comprised only half its strange beauty. Springing from each side of the breast, and ordinarily lying concealed under the wings, were little tufts of grayish feathers about two inches long and each terminated by a broad band of intense emerald green. These plumes can be raised at the will of the bird and spread out into a pair of elegant fans when the wings are elevated.

But this is not the only ornament. The two middle feathers of the tail are in the form of slender wires about five inches long, and which diverge in a beautiful double curve. About half an inch of the end of this wire is webbed on the outer side only, and colored of a fine metallic green and being curled spirally inward, form a pair of elegant glittering buttons, hanging five inches below the body and the same distance apart.

These two ornaments, the breast fans and the spiral-tipped tail wires, are altogether unique, not occurring on any other species of the eight thousand different birds that are known to exist upon the earth, and combined with the most exquisite beauty of plumage, render this one of the most perfectly lovely of the many lovely productions of nature. My transports of admiration and delight quite amused my Aroe hosts, who saw nothing more in the *burong raja* than we do in the robin or the goldfinch.

Thus one of my objects in coming to the Far

East was accomplished. I had obtained a specimen of the king bird of paradise (*Paradisaea regio*), which had been described by Linnaeus from skins preserved in a mutilated state by the natives. I knew how few Europeans had ever beheld the perfect little organism I now gazed upon and how very imperfectly it was still known in Europe.

The emotions excited in the mind of a naturalist who has long desired to see the actual thing which he has hitherto known only by description, drawing, or badly preserved external covering—especially when that thing is of surpassing rarity and beauty—require the poetic faculty fully to express them. The remote island in which I found myself situated, in an almost unvisited sea, far from the tracks of merchant fleets and navies; the wild, luxuriant tropical forest which stretched far away on every side; the rude, uncultured savages who gathered round me—all had their influence in determining the emotions with which I gazed upon this "thing of beauty."

I thought of the long ages of the past, during which the successive generations of this little creature had run their course, year by year being born and living and dying amid these dark and gloomy woods, with no intelligent eye to gaze upon their loveliness— to all appearance such a wanton waste of beauty. Such ideas excite a feeling of melancholy.

It seems sad that on the one hand such exquisite creatures should live out their lives and exhibit their charms only in these wild, inhospitable regions, doomed for ages yet to come to hopeless barbarism; while on the other hand, should civilized man ever reach these distant lands and bring moral, intellectual, and physical light into the recesses of these virgin forests, we may be sure that he will so disturb the nicely balanced relations of organic and inorganic nature as to cause the disappearance, and finally the extinction, of these very beings whose wonderful structure and beauty he alone is fitted to appreciate and enjoy.

This consideration must surely tell us that all living things were *not* made for man. Many of them have no relation to him. The cycle of their existence has gone on independently of his and is disturbed or broken by every advance in man's intellectual development; and their happiness and enjoyments, their loves and hates, their struggles for existence, their vigorous life and early death, would seem to be immediately related to their own well-being and perpetuation alone, limited only by the equal well-being and perpetuation of the numberless other organisms with which each is more or less intimately connected.

AN UNSUCCESSFUL SEARCH

. . . and [in April 1858] I found myself fairly established as the only European inhabitant of the vast island of New Guinea.

As we had some doubt about the natives, we slept at first with loaded guns beside us and a watch set; but after a few days, finding the people friendly and feeling sure that they would not venture to attack five well-armed men, we took no further precautions.

It appears, however, that Manokwari is not the place for birds of paradise, none of the natives being accustomed to preserve them. Those sold here are all brought from Amberbaki, about a hundred miles west, where the Manokwarians go to trade. . . .

After a month's close confinement in the house [because of a badly infected foot] I was at length able to go out a little, and about the same time I succeeded in getting a boat and six natives to take Ali and Lahagi to Amberbaki and to bring them back at the end of a month. Ali was charged to buy all the birds of paradise he could get and to shoot and skin all other rare or new birds, and Lahagi was to collect insects, which I hoped might be more abundant than at Manokwari. . . .

My men now returned from Amberbaki, but alas! brought me almost nothing. They had visited several villages and even went two days' journey into the interior, but could find no skins of birds of paradise to purchase, except the common kind, and very few of those. The birds found were the same as at Manokwari, but were still scarcer.

None of the natives anywhere near the coast shoot or prepare birds of paradise, which come from far in the interior over two or three ranges of mountains, passing by barter from village to village till they reach the sea. There the natives of Manokwari buy them, and on their return home sell them to the Bugis or Ternate traders. It is therefore hopeless for a traveler to go to any particular place on the coast of New Guinea where rare paradise birds may have been bought in hopes of obtaining freshly killed specimens from the natives; and it also shows the scarcity of these birds in any one locality, since from the Amberbaki district, a celebrated place, where at least five or six species have been procured, not one of the rare ones has been obtained this year. . . .

On the 22nd of July the schooner *Hester Helena* arrived, and five days afterward we bade adieu to Manokwari without much regret, for in no place which I have visited have I encountered more privations and annoyances. Continual rain, continual sickness, little wholesome food, with a plague of ants and flies surpassing anything I had before met with, required all a naturalist's ardor to encounter; and when they were uncompensated by great success in collecting, became all the more insupportable.

This long-thought-of and much-desired voyage to New Guinea had realized none of my expectations. Instead of being far better than the Aroe Islands, it was in almost everything much worse. Instead of producing several of the rarer paradise birds, I had not even seen one of them, and had not obtained any one superlatively fine bird or insect.

I cannot deny, however, that Manokwari was very rich in ants. One small black kind was excessively abundant. Almost every shrub and tree was more or less infested with it, and its large papery nests were everywhere to be seen. They immediately took possession of my house, building a large nest in the roof and forming papery tunnels down almost every post.

They swarmed on my table as I was at work setting out my insects, carrying them off from under my very nose and even tearing them from the cards on which they were gummed if I left them for an instant. They crawled continually over my hands and face and got into my hair and roamed at will over my whole body, not producing much inconvenience till they began to bite, which they would do on meeting with any obstruction to their passage, and with a sharpness which made me jump again and rush to undress and turn out the offender.

They visited my bed also, so that night brought no relief from their persecutions; and I verily believe that during my three and a half months' residence at Manokwari I was never for a single hour entirely free from them. They were not nearly so voracious as many other kinds, but their numbers and ubiquity rendered it necessary to be constantly on guard against them.

The flies that troubled me most were a large kind of bluebottle or blowfly. These settled in swarms on my bird skins when first put out to dry, filling their plumage with masses of eggs which, if neglected, the next day produced maggots. They would get under the wings or under the body where it rested on the drying board, sometimes actually raising it up half an inch by the mass of eggs deposited in a few hours; and every egg was so firmly glued to the fibers of the feathers as to make it a work of much time and patience to get them off without injuring the bird. In no other locality have I ever been troubled with such a plague as this.

A NEW SPECIES

The morning after I had got into my new house [on the Moluccan island of Batjan in October 1858], I sent my boys out to shoot and went myself to explore the road to the coal mines. . . .

Just as I got home, I overtook Ali returning from shooting with some birds hanging from his belt. He seemed much pleased, and said, "Look here, sir, what a curious bird," holding out what at first completely puzzled me. I saw a bird with a mass of splendid green feathers on its breast, elongated into two glittering tufts; but what I could not understand was a pair of long white feathers which stuck straight out from each shoulder. Ali assured me that the bird stuck them out this way itself when fluttering its wings, and that they had remained so without his touching them. I now saw that I had got a great prize, no less than a completely new form of the bird of paradise, differing most remarkably from every other known bird.

The general plumage is very sober, being a pure ashy olive with a purplish tinge on the back; the crown of the head is beautifully glossed with pale metallic violet, and the feathers of the front extend as much over the beak as in most of the family. The neck and breast are scaled with fine metallic green, and the feathers on the lower part are elongated on each side, so as to form a two-pointed gorget, which can be folded beneath the wings or partially erected and spread out in the same way as the side plumes of most of the birds of paradise.

The four long white plumes which give the bird its altogether unique character spring from little tubercles close to the upper edge of the shoulder or bend of the wing; they are narrow, gently curved, and equally webbed on both sides, of a pure creamy-white color. They are about six inches long, equaling the wing, and can be raised at right angles to it or laid along the body at the pleasure of the bird. The bill is horn color, the legs yellow, and the iris pale olive.

This striking novelty has been named by Mr. G. R. Gray of the British Museum, *Semioptera wallacei,* or "Wallace's standard wing."

The female bird is remarkably plain, being entirely of a dull, pale earthy brown, with only a slight tinge of ashy violet on the head to relieve its general monotony; and the young males exactly resemble her.

This bird frequents the lower trees of the forests, and like most paradise birds, is in constant motion—flying from branch to branch, clinging to the twigs and even to the smooth and vertical trunks almost as easily as a woodpecker. It continually utters a harsh, creaking note. . . . The males at short intervals open and flutter their wings, erect the long shoulder feathers, and spread out the elegant green breast shields.

The standard wing is found in Halmahera as well as in Batjan and all the specimens from the former island have the green breast shield rather longer, the crown of the head darker violet, and the lower parts of the body rather more strongly scaled with green. This is the only paradise bird yet found in the Moluccan district, all the others being confined to the Papuan [New Guinea] Islands and North Australia.

The true paradise birds are omnivorous, feeding on fruits and insects—of the former preferring the small figs; of the latter, grasshoppers, locusts, and phasmas [stick insects], as well as cockroaches and caterpillars. When I returned home in 1862, I was so fortunate as to find two adult males of this species [lesser bird of paradise] in Singapore; and as they seemed healthy, and fed voraciously on rice, bananas, and cockroaches, I determined on giving the very high price asked for them—£100—and to bring them to England by the overland route under my own care.

On my way home I stayed a week at Bombay, to break the journey and to lay in a fresh stock of bananas for my birds. I had great difficulty, however, in supplying them with insect food, for in the Peninsular and Oriental steamers cockroaches were scarce, and it was only by setting traps in the storerooms, and by hunting an hour every night in the forecastle that I could secure a few dozen of these creatures—scarcely enough for a single meal.

The journey to Suez offered no particular incident and the birds continued in good health, as did two or three lories [Far Eastern parrots] I had brought. But with the railway journey to Alexandria difficulties began. It was in February, and the night was clear and frosty. The railway officials made difficulties, and it was only by representing the rarity and value of the birds that I could have the cage placed in a box-truck.

When we got into the Mediterranean the weather became suddenly cold, and worse still, I found that the ship was free from cockroaches. As I thought that animal food was perhaps necessary to counteract the cold, I felt afraid for the safety of my charge and determined to stay a fortnight at Malta in order to reach England a little later, and also to lay in a store of the necessary food. I accordingly arranged to break my voyage there, went to a hotel, and found that I could get unlimited cockroaches at a baker's close by.

At Marseilles I again had trouble, but at last succeeded in getting them [the birds] placed in a guard's van, with permission to enter and feed them en route. Passing through France it was a sharp frost, but they did not seem to suffer; and when we reached London, I was glad to transfer them into the care of Mr. Bart-

lett, who conveyed them to the Zoological Gardens.
Thus ended my Malayan travels.

■ This homecoming was different. The youthful surveyor of many years ago had at last become a sci-
entist himself. His reputation had been established
not only by his paper on natural selection but also by
other important papers he had sent home to London,
and he was now on friendly terms with the leaders of
the scientific world—Darwin, Lyell, Hooker, Huxley.
Although he arrived home too late for the first great
excitement over the publication of Darwin's *Origin
of Species,* he was part of the new era it ushered in,
and he went on from here to make many other original contributions to evolutionary theory.

Wallace returned to England in 1862, but his
book on his travels was not published until 1869.
With his collections about him, he spent several years
studying them and writing up his conclusions before
turning to the account of his travels, encouraged by
Darwin as Bates had been. And this time he succeeded, for his *Malay Archipelago* is ranked with the
books of Darwin and Bates as among the best such
ever written—full of interesting observations, marvelous descriptions and fascinating adventures.

Unlike Bates, however, Wallace never settled
down to a permanent job, although he made several
unsuccessful efforts to find one. Instead he wrote
books and numerous articles, and he also made a
lecture tour of the United States. But he made many
changes of residence, although all in the vicinity of
London, and some poor investments, and so he continued to be pressed for money. In 1880, while Glad-
stone was Prime Minister, the British government

awarded him an annual pension in honor of his scientific achievements, and this relieved Wallace of his most pressing financial worries for the rest of his life.

His active and restless mind also led him into fields outside of biology, such as land reform, anti-vaccination, and spiritualism, and some of his stands were unpopular. But his claims to fame in the scientific world are secure, and some of his books are still considered classics, particularly *The Geographical Distribution of Animals*, published in 1876, and *Island Life*, published in 1880.

In the aftermath of the excitement produced by Darwin's book, *On the Origin of Species*, some of those most closely involved, including Hooker and Darwin himself, wavered on the importance of natural selection. But Wallace always gave it first place in the process of formation of new species, and he published a book entitled *Darwinism* in 1889 to uphold this view.

Wallace's long and fruitful life came to an end on November 17, 1913. Suggestions that he be buried in Westminster Abbey were turned down by the family, and he was buried instead in a little cemetery in Broadstone, where he had made his last home. But on November 1, 1915, memorial plaques to three great men were unveiled in Westminster Abbey—one to Lord Lister, the founder of modern antiseptic surgery, and the others to Wallace and to Hooker—"to men who," said the dean of the Abbey, "I believe, will always be ranked among the most eminent scientists of the last century."

epilogue

Although I maintain, and even enforce, my
differences from some of Darwin's views,
my whole work tends forcibly to illustrate
the overwhelming importance of natural
selection over all other agencies in the production of new species.

WALLACE, *Darwinism*

THE THEORY OF
NATURAL SELECTION

> . . . natural selection, often by a compro-
> mise between conflicting environmental de-
> mands, determines how animals live and
> not how they die.
>
> MURTON, *Ibis*

■ If the earth and all its inhabitants were created in the year 4004 B.C., as calculated by Usher, there would be no problem in accounting for the origin of species. Clearly they would all have been "created" at the same time a few thousand years ago, although the process of "creation" would still be a mystery. Part and parcel of this belief was the assumption that everything had been created solely for man's use. Gradually, however, these ideas came to be challenged.

But first, something should be said about science. It is easy to misunderstand science and scientific method. Science does not do away with beauty or ethics. Instead, it is limited by definition to what

203

can be observed and measured. It is a servant that can be used to discover how things work, and in doing so, it reveals an underlying order. But it makes no claims to explaining the ultimate why, nor is it a substitute for systems of ethics. And one has only to read Wallace's and Bates's vivid descriptions to see that interest in science does not exclude appreciation of beauty.

Historical geology, the scientific study of the history of the earth, has played an important role in the challenge to established thinking. It is now known that the earth is about a million times older than was thought. Its long history might be compared to a moving picture. At first we had only the last frame, representing the present, to look at, and so it was thought that this was the way things were in the beginning.

Gradually other frames were brought into focus, but they were only bits and pieces of the whole story, scattered here and there over an immensity of time and without any grand unifying theme. Evolution by means of natural selection was to provide one such theme, and that is why it is a major milestone in our progress toward an understanding of our world.

Fossils are a part of the past history of both geology and biology, and they show that some plants and animals, different from those of the present day, have at various times become extinct. This poses a new question, for if some earlier creatures died out, where did the later ones come from? If there is extinction, there must also be "creation." This was the problem that attracted Wallace and Bates.

Lyell had not been able to solve it, although he tried. First of all, he believed in permanent unchanging species. As a geologist, he was quite familiar with the fossil remains of earlier plants and animals. But he rejected Lamarck's contention that these plants and animals had changed gradually into the species we know today and that the fossils were merely records of the changes made along the way. Instead, fossils were gravestones marking the death (extinction) of an unchanging species. (Actually, some species have become completely extinct, and others have evolved). How then to account for the appearance of new species? Lyell could only suggest vaguely that they were somehow inconspicuously "created" at irregular times and in widely separated places.

Varieties were a different matter. Children, manifestly produced by natural means, obviously differ from their parents. Lyell had to admit the plain fact that species varied, although he claimed that the amount of variation possible was strictly limited, thus preserving a species intact. But he was neither a biologist nor a collector or he might have changed his mind about the limits to variation.

Wallace and Bates came to see that there were no such fixed limits to the amount of variation. They examined thousands of specimens in their long years of collecting. If they followed Lyell, some, the species, were mysteriously created; while others, the varieties, were born of living parents. Looked at a few at a time, this might even seem reasonable. But Wallace alone collected more than 125,000 specimens in the Malay Archipelago, and he could see that there was a wide range of variation. To pick an arbitrary point, as some did, and say that those organisms which varied less were merely varieties produced by ordinary reproduction and that those which varied more were species specially created, came to seem nonsensical. Such a division could not rationally be made. Therefore, all must be produced by the ordinary process of reproduction.

Lyell had missed another clue that geology might have given him, that there is a relationship between a species and its immediate predecessors. Wallace, in his first major paper (written in Sarawak in Borneo), explained this in the following words: "Every species has come into existence coincident both in space and time with a pre-existing closely allied species." By this he meant evolution, the gradual change of one species into another that would thus be related to the earlier one by descent. This explained what had so puzzled Lyell, why the creation of new species is so hard to observe. It is not a sudden event but a gradual happening.

But granted the fact of change and the assumption of evolution, the next question was, what could be the mechanism of change? How could a change have come about? Do organisms change merely for the sake of changing? In fact, why should there be any change at all? The theory of evolution by itself was not enough to give the answers. Lamarck and Chambers had been partially right in suggesting that the answers involved natural means of reproduction and the inheritance of characteristics (although not of acquired ones). But other parts of their theories were questionable, and so the problem was still up in the air.

For a traveling naturalist like Wallace, there were still other clues. It had been assumed that similar climatic regions would have similar inhabitants. But Wallace traveled in three of the four tropical regions of the earth (he never got to Africa), and in each he found a differing set. "Borneo and New Guinea, as alike physically as two distinct countries can be, are zoologically wide as the poles asunder," and they both differ as much from the South American tropics (behind this, of course, lies the theory of continental drift). Nevertheless, in each Wallace found a harmony of relationships among the plants and animals, a harmony that also exists on a smaller scale on islands, where each is again a little world to itself.

Islands are small natural systems that are more or less self-contained. The diversity of life that has developed in these unique environments is fascinating and provocative. Darwin had been deeply impressed by the strange forms of life he found on the different islands of the Galapagos Archipelago, six hundred miles off Ecuador in the Pacific Ocean. Wallace was intrigued by Darwin's account of them in his *Voyage of the Beagle*, and he had an opportunity to observe for himself some of the equally strange forms that have developed on islands of the Malay Archipelago. (The recent appearance of a new volcanic island, named Surtsey, off the southern coast of Iceland, has given present-day biologists an exceptional chance to observe such development from its beginning.)

What could be the explanation for the harmonious development of such diverse groupings of animals and plants?

At this point, Wallace added Malthus and his principle of population to his mix of ideas. Population pressure means many things. Malthus was concerned about its moral effect on man. Wallace, on the other hand, considered what happened in the natural world. It becomes clear, whatever aspect one emphasizes, that life represents a balance of forces, a compromise.

More animals and plants are produced than live to reproduce, and this is the crucial point: for it is the ones which reproduce that pass on their characteristics to the next generation. Which ones are they? As a rule, they are those best adapted to the circumstances in which they live; no plant or animal lives in a vacuum.

If the world were limited to cats and mice, one might think that the "perfect" cat would be one able to catch every mouse. But this would mean its automatic extinction, as there would be nothing left for it to eat. Instead, some cats catch some mice. The surviving cats pass their mouse-catching ability on to their offspring, and the surviving mice pass their cat-escaping ability on to theirs.

All mice perform some function. Those which are caught enable the cats to go on living, those which are not enable the mice to go on living. As for the cats, their ability to catch mice is also continuously being tested, and those best able to do so are the ones which will live to reproduce, passing on to the next generation those characteristics most useful in mouse-catching. Thus there is continuous change, the cats improving in their ability to catch mice and the mice improving in their ability to escape. In other words, the changes are not random. They are a compromise worked out under the actual conditions under which these animals are living.

As a rule, these changes are gradual. Large or abrupt changes either in the environment or in the animal usually mean the death of an individual or the extinction of a species. If cats suddenly became twice as big, or mice twice as small, the cats would starve for want of sufficent food.

"Varieties" are the equivalent of gradual changes, and Wallace now saw where they fitted in to the scheme of things. "Most or perhaps all the variations from the typical form of a species must have some definite effect, however slight, on the habits or capacities of the individuals," and these effects will be either good or bad, useful or harmful. The animal or plant having a useful variation—for instance, the mouse that escapes a little quicker—will be more likely to survive, and it will pass this useful characteristic on to its offspring. In other words, this useful characteristic will be selected.

The conviction that a species varied only within narrow limits was based on what happens to domesticated animals turned wild. They do tend to return to the wild type, but there is a reason for this. Domesticated animals are artificially selected, and their balance or compromise is maintained by man. Such animals are not in harmony with a wild environment and they cannot maintain themselves without man's help. Turned wild, they must revert to something like the wild type, if that is still possible, or die.

Wild animals, on the contrary, are in tune with their environments (providing that changes in it are gradual). In this sense, each succeeding variety is "superior" to the preceding ones because it is better adapted to the present circumstances. Such animals cannot revert to an earlier type unless their environment also changes back. Obviously this doesn't happen. Instead, varieties tend "to depart indefinitely from the original type," resulting in the course of time in new species distinct from the old ones.

At last Wallace felt he had the answer. He quickly wrote out a sketch of it, in February 1858, and sent it to Darwin from Ternate, little dreaming what the result of this would be.

Wallace had begun to correspond with Darwin in October 1856. The one answering letter he had so far received had made it clear that Darwin himself had been working for twenty years on the same question, how species and varieties differed from each other. But Darwin had explained nothing about his theory of natural selection, and Wallace had no inkling that he had hit upon the same theory when he sent his outline to Darwin.

Darwin had come to this theory by a somewhat different route. Nevertheless, his and Wallace's theories were essentially the same, the origin of species by means of natural selection. Darwin's friends Lyell and Hooker had both urged him to publish his theory, and he had already been hard at work for more than two years on such a book when Wallace's paper arrived on June 18, 1858.

This was a calamity. What should be done now? Hooker and Lyell suggested a solution, that Wallace's paper and some excerpts from what Darwin had already written but not yet published be read at a meeting of the Linnean Society of London. And so, what have become known as the "joint papers" were read two weeks later, on July 1. Wallace did not learn of this outcome until October. As a self-educated collector, he was "highly gratified" to have at last attracted the attention of some of "the most eminent naturalists in England."

Wallace had planned to write a book on the theory himself, but this now proved unnecessary. Darwin set to work again, making an "abstract" of the larger work he had originally planned, and finally, in November 1859, his *Origin of Species by Means of Natural Selection* was published.

It was left to Bates and his theory of mimicry, however, to provide one of the most dramatic demonstrations of how natural selection works. Darwin was delighted with the theory. Death and extinction are a great deal easier to observe than is the accumlation of gradual changes leading to the formation of new species. The theory of mimicry showed how this could happen.

It explained how a rare, palatable species of butterfly could come to resemble a common, conspicuous, but unpalatable species living in the same area. Those most unlike the unpalatable ones would be eaten, those most like them would be avoided and would survive to reproduce their kind. What might have been at first an accidental similarity is refined generation after generation until one becomes a counterfeit of the other. But it is only a counterfeit, not an exact duplicate, for the similarities are only superficial, just enough to fool a predator.

Bates had to guess about the unpalatability. This has since been proved, and the reason for it is now known. Larvae of the protected butterflies feed on plants producing substances distasteful to predators, while larvae of the unprotected butterflies do not. And recently, chemical analysis of our common monarch butterfly (which is mimicked by the viceroy) has shown that besides having a bitter taste, it is also an indigestible poison to most predators. Its larvae eat plants containing digitalis-like substances that are heart poisons. For predators, learning to avoid such insects is not simply a matter of taste but of life and death.

The protected butterflies are usually brightly colored, and this warns predators that have once tasted them to stay away. Their mimics have a similar coloration and are thus also protected. The mimicry is maintained because deviations are eaten.

Wallace came across some even more complicated cases of mimicry in the Malay Archipelago. In these there were several forms of the female of a species, some of which resemble different distasteful butterflies. This extraordinary situation is known as mimetic polymorphism.

Mimicry differs from convergence, as Bates pointed out. There is a direct relationship of cause and effect between the mimicked species and its copy. There is no such direct relationship between convergent species such as the hummingbird and hawkmoth. They do not necessarily live in the same area, although they may, and their similarity is not kept up by a common predator. It is based instead on a similar method of obtaining food, here the sipping of nectar from flowers. But even here they do not compete directly with each other, for hummingbirds feed in the daytime and hawkmoths at night, dividing up the ecological niche. There are, of course, still other kinds of similarities that are due to family relationships, to descent from a common ancestor.

Bates's theory of mimicry was first proposed in

one of a series of scientific papers that he wrote about the insects of the Amazon Valley. This one was on the butterfly family Heliconidae and, appropriately enough, it was also read at a meeting of the Linnean Society of London, in November 1861, and published in 1862.

"A MOST BEAUTIFUL PROOF"

[BATES] The most interesting part of the natural history of the Heliconidae is the mimetic analogies of which a great many of the species are the objects. Mimetic analogies, it is scarcely necessary to observe, are resemblances in external appearance, shape, and colors between members of widely distinct families: an idea of what is meant may be formed by supposing a pigeon to exist with the general figure and plumage of a hawk. . . .

These imitative resemblances, of which hundreds of instances could be cited, are full of interest, and fill us with the greater astonishment the closer we investigate them, for some show a minute and palpably intentional likeness which is perfectly staggering. I have found that those features of the portrait are most attended to by nature which produce the most effective deception when the insects are seen in nature. The faithfulness of the resemblance, in many cases, is not so striking when they are seen in the cabinet. Although I had daily practice in insect collecting for many years and was always on my guard, I was constantly being deceived by them in the woods.

Every species in nature may be looked upon as maintaining its existence by virtue of some endowment enabling it to withstand the host of adverse circumstances by which it is surrounded. The means are of endless diversity. Some are provided with special organs of offense, others have passive means of holding their own in the battle of life. Great fecundity is generally of much avail, added to capabilities, active or passive, of wide dispersion: so that when the species is extirpated in one part of its area of distribution, the place is refilled by migration of individuals from another part. A great number have means of concealment from their enemies, of one sort or another. Many are enabled to escape extermination or obtain subsistence by disguises of various kinds: amongst these must be reckoned the adaptive resemblance of an otherwise defenseless species to one whose flourishing race shows that it enjoys peculiar advantages. . . . It is probable they are unpalatable to insect enemies. . . .

The process by which a mimetic analogy is brought about in nature is a problem which involves that of the origin of all species and all adaptations.

The explanation of this seems to be quite clear on the theory of natural selection, as recently expounded by Mr. Darwin in the *Origin of Species*. The local varieties or races cannot be supposed to have been formed by the direct action of physical conditions on the individuals, because in limited districts where these conditions are the same, the most widely contrasted varieties are found existing together, and it is inexplicable how they could have produced the nice adaptations which these diverse varieties exhibit. . . . Neither can these adapted races, as before remarked, have originated in one generation by *sports* or a single act of variation in each case.

It is clear, therefore, that some other active principle must be here at work to draw out, as it were, steadily in certain directions the suitable variations which arise, generation after generation, until forms have resulted which . . . are considerably different from their parent as well as their sister forms. This principle can be no other than natural selection, the selecting agents being insectivorous animals, which gradually destroy those sports or varieties that are not sufficiently like [the species mimicked] to deceive them. . . .

If a mimetic species varies, some of its varieties must be more and some less faithful imitations of the object mimicked. According, therefore, to the closeness of its persecution by enemies, who seek the imitator but avoid the imitated, will be its tendency to become an exact counterfeit—the less perfect degrees of resemblance being, generation after generation, eliminated, and only the others left to propagate their kind. . . .

Such, I conceive, is the only way in which the origin of mimetic species can be explained. I believe the case offers a most beautiful proof of the truth of the theory of natural selection. It also shows that a new adaptation, or the formation of a new species, is not effected by great and sudden change, but by numerous small steps of natural variation and selection. . . .

I have not thought it necessary to mention cases of close resemblances in insects which are only accidental or which are explicable by the blood relationship or affinity existing between the species which display them. Some orders of insects contain an almost infinite variety of forms, and it will not be wonderful, therefore, if species here and there be found to resemble each other, although inhabiting opposite parts of the earth and belonging to widely different families. Such analogies are accidental, and can have nothing at all to do with the evidently intentional system of resemblances, carried on from place to place, which I have discussed.

Some cosmopolitan families present very similar species in all parts of the earth; it can scarcely be necessary to say that close resemblances between New and Old World forms in these cases are resemblances of affinity, and not mimetic analogies. The conditions of life of these creatures are different in each locality where one or more separate local forms prevail, and those conditions are the selecting agents. . . .

It may be remarked that a mimetic species need not always be a rare one, although this is very generally the case. . . .

The operation of selecting agents, gradually and steadily bringing about the deceptive resemblance of a species to some other definite object, produces the impression of there being some innate principle which causes an advance or organization in a special direction. It seems as though the proper variation always arose in the species and the mimicry were a predestined goal. This suggested the only other explanation that I have heard of, namely that there may be an innate tendency in the organization to become modified in a given direction—or that the parent insect, being powerfully affected by the desire of concealment from the enemies of its race, may transmit peculiarities to its offspring that help it to become modified, and thus, in the course of many generations, the species becomes gradually assimilated to other forms or objects [a Lamarckian explanation based on inheritance of acquired characteristics]. On examination, however, these explanations are found to be untenable, and the appearances which suggest them illusory.

Those who earnestly desire a rational explanation, must, I think, arrive at the conclusion that these apparently miraculous, but always beautiful and wonderful, mimetic resemblances, and therefore probably every other kind of adaptation in beings, are brought about by agencies similar to those we have here discussed.

■Bates and Wallace would have been pleased with some more recently discovered evidence, the case of industrial melanism. Within the past one hundred years the colors of moths in various places in England have changed from predominantly gray, with an occasional black one, to predominantly black with an occasional gray one. (The moths are what is known as "polymorphic," that is, they normally occur in more than one color and are either light or dark. In the same way, our common screech owl has two color phases, and the birds are either reddish in color or gray.) The surprising reason behind the change in the numbers of dark and light moths is the industrial revolution.

The moths rest during the day on the trunks of trees. They are protected by their color from being eaten by birds, gray moths on gray bark being nearly invisible. However, smoke from nearby factories has gradually blackened the bark of the trees, and now it is the dark moths that are protected and the light ones that are conspicuous and eaten. The result of this selection by birds has been, in the space of a century, a complete reversal in the predominant color.

This shows natural selection in action, proving that it does operate, and very efficiently, too. It also demonstrates that natural selection can take advantage only of characteristics that already exist; it can't invent them. As Bates remarked in regard to the toucan's bill, nature must use what is available. In the same way, if it had not been for the occasional dark ones, the moths would now be altogether extinct in the industrial regions, for the light ones would have been eaten.

There is a still more serious implication to this, however. This sort of change has been going on without anyone's being aware of it, until recently. Who would have thought that the industrial revolution could or would affect the colors of moths? At the same time this serves as a warning, a warning of the speed with which such unintended and seemingly unrelated effects accumulate.

Natural selection, like politics, is an art of the possible, a compromise. And compromises, by their very nature, can rarely be made instantaneously, nor can they be permanent. The complexity of the natural world insures continuous change, and this requires the continuing adjustment of every part. It has led, over millions and billions of years, to the world as we know it.

An understanding of the importance and the delicacy of the resulting interrelationships is essential if man is not to destroy carelessly what has been so long in the making, for he is a comparative newcomer to an ancient system. Science is the effort to acquire that knowledge and understanding. We owe a debt to people like Wallace and Bates who by their determination have helped in this endeavor.

Chronology
Glossary
For Further Reading
Sources and Notes
Index

Chronology

HENRY WALTER BATES

May 1848– *Sept. 1849*	Belém and vicinity, and Tocantins River
Sept. 1849– *May 1850*	Up Amazon River to Manaus, and then on to Tefé on Upper Amazon
April–Nov. 1851	Belém
Nov. 1851–1855	Headquarters at Santarém; many trips in vicinity, including Tapajoz River
1855–Feb. 1859	Headquarters at Tefé; went as far up Upper Amazon as São Paulo
Feb.–July 1859	Return trip to England

ALFRED RUSSEL WALLACE

May 1848– *Aug. 1849*	Belém and vicinity, and Tocantins River
Aug.–Dec. 1849	Up Amazon River to Manaus
Aug. 1850	Up Rio Negro; reached farthest point (Javita) Mar. 1851
June 1851	First trip up Uaupés River
Sept. 1851	Return to Manaus
Oct. 1851	Second trip up Uaupés River; reached farthest point (Mitú) Mar. 1852
Mar.–Oct. 1852	Return trip to England
April–Oct. 1854	Singapore and vicinity
Nov. 1854– *Jan. 1856*	Sarawak, Borneo
Jan.–May 1856	Singapore
June 13–15, 1856	Bali
June 17–Aug. 30	Lombok
Sept.–Dec. 1856	Celebes
Jan.–July 1857	Aroe Islands

July–Nov. 1857	Celebes; then Timor, Banda, and Amboina
Jan. 1858–Jan. 1861	Ternate in the Moluccas, his headquarters for three years
April–July 1858	New Guinea
Oct. 1858–April 1859	Batjan
July–Sept. 1860	Waigeo; and visits to many other islands
1861	Timor, Banda, Boeroe, Celebes, Java, Sumatra
Feb.–April 1862	Singapore to London

Glossary

ACQUIRED CHARACTERISTICS. Responses to the environment, such as muscles strengthened by exercise, through habit or will. These changes are nongenetic and thus cannot be inherited.

ADAPTATION. Adjustment to the environment based on genetic inheritance.

AESTIVATION. An inactive state during the summer or dry season.

ARCHIPELAGO. A sea studded with islands; a group of islands.

BATESIAN MIMICRY. The resemblance of a rare, edible insect (usually) to a common, conspicuous, inedible one; discovered by Henry Walter Bates. *See also* mimicry, protective coloration.

BIOLOGY. The study of living things.

BOTANY. The study of plants.

CAMPOS. Tropical grasslands of Brazil, with an average annual rainfall of around twenty inches per year, less than one-tenth that received in the wettest tropical rain forest.

CATASTROPHIST. One who believes that all life on earth has been wiped out at different times in the past by sudden, overwhelming catastrophes.

COLEOPTERA. Largest order of insects, containing beetles and weevils.

CONTINENTAL DRIFT. Relative displacements of the continents, for convenience often measured from Africa as a base. About three hundred million years ago, according to Alfred Wegener, all continents were part of one large continent, which he called *Pangea*. It has since broken into parts, which have slowly "drifted" to their present positions.

CONTINENTAL SHELF. The shallow sea bed bordering the continents, generally about six hundred feet deep or less; part of the adjacent land mass in dry periods. Off the continental shelf the sea bed drops sharply to six thousand feet or more, forming a steep cliff.

CONVERGENT EVOLUTION. Similarities in form between distantly related organisms, such as hummingbirds and hawkmoths, or whales and fishes, which live under similar conditions.

Glossary

DIPTEROUS. Belonging to insect order containing true flies, mosquitoes, gnats, etc.

ENTOMOLOGY. The study of insects.

EVOLUTION. Gradual accumulation of small changes in organisms over many generations, leading to new species; descent with modification. *See also* Lamarckism, natural selection, species.

FAMILY. A group of animals or plants of similar genera.

FOSSILS. The remains or traces of animals or plants that lived long ago. They may be records either of steps in the evolution of species or of dead-end species that became completely extinct and left no descendants. Even today less than 1 per cent of the species that have existed are represented by fossils.

GALLINACEOUS. Belonging to bird order containing pheasants, turkeys, grouse, etc.

GENETICS. The study of variations and resemblances among individuals and their inheritance, the details of which were almost completely unknown a hundred years ago.

GENUS (pl. GENERA). A group of animals or plants of similar species.

GEOGRAPHICAL DISTRIBUTION. The ranges of plants and animals; the study of where they are and why.

GEOLOGY. The study of the earth and what it is made of.

GLACIER. A large mass of ice forming in polar regions or on mountaintops. Glaciers increased greatly in size during the Ice Age or Pleistocene (*q.v.*).

HYMENOPTEROUS. Belonging to insect order containing bees, wasps, and ants.

ICE AGE. See Pleistocene.

IGAPÓ. Amazonian floodland, where forest is submerged part of the year.

INDUSTRIAL MELANISM. The increasing frequency of darker individuals among moth populations in smoke-polluted areas. *See also* melanism.

LAMARCKISM. The theory of evolution proposed by Lamarck, in which characteristics acquired by habit or will are inherited, leading to the gradual formation of new species. *See also* acquired characteristics, evolution, natural selection.

LEPIDOPTERA. Insect order containing butterflies and moths.

MALTHUS' "PRINCIPLE OF POPULATION." "The power of

223

population is indefinitely greater than the power in the earth to produce subsistence for man. Population, when unchecked, increases in a geometrical ratio. Subsistence increases only in an arithmetical ratio."

MELANISM. Unusual darkening of normal coloration; the darker of two color forms. *See also* industrial melanism.

METAMORPHOSIS. Rapid change from larval to adult form of animals.

MIMETIC POLYMORPHISM. Unusual case of mimicry in which females of an unprotected species of butterfly resemble butterflies of one or more protected species. *See also* Batesian mimicry, mimicry, polymorphism.

MIMICRY. A form of protective coloration in which defenseless animals (usually insects) resemble better-protected ones, or other objects such as leaves or twigs. *See also* Batesian mimicry, mimetic polymorphism, protective coloration.

NATURAL SELECTION. Selection by the environment. Those individuals better adapted to the environment are more likely to survive and reproduce their kind. Continued generation after generation, the inheritance of small differences or changes leads to the formation of new species. *See also* adaptation, evolution, species, varieties.

ORIGIN OF SPECIES. *See* evolution, natural selection.

ORNITHOLOGY. The study of birds.

PHOTOSYNTHESIS. Process in which green plants synthesize organic compounds from water and carbon dioxide, using energy absorbed from sunlight.

PHYLUM (pl. PHYLA). A major division of animals or plants, such as arthropods (crustaceans, insects, spiders, etc.), or chordates (fishes, amphibians, reptiles, birds, and mammals).

PLEISTOCENE (ICE AGE). The most recent geological period, perhaps including the present, which began from one to three million years ago and was characterized by widespread glaciers.

POLYMORPHISM. Occurring in several different forms at the same time, as red and gray foxes or red and gray screech owls.

PREDATOR. An animal that kills and eats another.

PROTECTIVE COLORATION (protective imitation, protective resemblance). Coloration of an animal that makes it inconspicuous to its predators. Occasionally the coloration is conspicuous and acts as a warning of bad taste to prospective predators. *See also* Batesian mimicry, mimicry.

SPECIES. An interbreeding group of organisms. At any one time species are separated from one another by various barriers to interbreeding. Considered over a period of time, however, each one is related to its immediate predecessor by descent. *See also* evolution, fossils, natural selection.

TRANSMUTATION OF SPECIES. The gradual change of one species into another; a term used by Lamarck. *See also* Lamarckism.

TROPICAL RAIN FOREST. Dense, luxuriant forest which grows in regions where rainfall averages from under 100 inches to over 300 inches per year and where temperature averages about eighty degrees Fahrenheit.

TROPICS. Region lying between Tropic of Cancer and Tropic of Capricorn, with the equator in the middle. *See also* campos, igapó, tropical rain forest.

VARIATION. Inherited or acquired differences between individuals of a species. *See also* acquired characteristics, adaptation.

VARIETIES. Here, differing individuals of a species.

WALLACE'S LINE. An imaginary line drawn between the islands of Bali and Lombok, between Borneo and Celebes and south of the Philippines. It marks the division of the Malay Archipelago into two parts in which the animals differ greatly; discovered by Alfred Russel Wallace.

ZOOLOGY. The study of animals.

For Further Reading

"On the Tendency of Species to Form Varieties; and On the Perpetuation of Varieties and Species by Natural Means of Selection." Charles Darwin and Alfred Wallace, in *Journal of the Linnean Society of London* (*Zoology*), III (1858), 45–62. (Read July 1 and published August 20, 1858; known as the "joint papers.")

"Butterflies and Plants." Paul R. Ehrlich and Peter H. Raven, in *Scientific American*, CCXVI (June 1967), 105–13 (Mimicry.)

"Feathered Dancers of Little Tobago." E. Thomas Gilliard and Frederick Kent Truslow, in *National Geographic*, CXIV (Sept. 1958), 428–40. (Greater birds of paradise.)

"The Confirmation of Continental Drift." Patrick M. Hurley, in *Scientific American*, CCXVIII (April 1968), 53–64.

"Darwin's Missing Evidence." H. B. D. Kettlewell, in *Scientific American*, CC (March 1959), 48–53. (Industrial melanism.)

"Lateritic Soils." Mary McNeil, in *Scientific American*, CCXI (Nov. 1964), 97–102.

"Science Explores the Monsoon Sea." Samuel W. Matthews and Robert F. Sisson, in *National Geographic*, CXXXII (Oct. 1967), 554–75. (Continental drift.)

"Surtsey—Island Born of Fire." Sigurdur Thorarinsson, in *National Geographic*, CXXVII (May 1965), 713–26. (Volcanic island.)

Sources and Notes

SOURCES

The works from which selections have been chosen are abbreviated below, and the abbreviations are used in the Notes that follow. Numbers at the left in the Notes represent pages in this edition on which specific selections appear.

HENRY WALTER BATES

"Lepidoptera: Heliconidae"   "Contributions to an Insect Fauna of the Amazon Valley. Lepidoptera: Heliconidae" in *Transactions of the Linnean Society of London*, XXIII (1862), 495–515.

Naturalist on the Amazons   *The Naturalist on the River Amazons.* London, 1863; rev. edn., 1864. Revised edition reprinted, Berkeley, Calif., University of California Press, 1962. Unless otherwise indicated, the 1962 edition is the source.

THOMAS HENRY HUXLEY

Man's Place in Nature   *Man's Place in Nature.* London, 1863. Reprinted, Ann Arbor, Mich., University of Michigan Press, 1959 (the present source).

JAMES MARCHANT, ed.

Alfred Russel Wallace   *Alfred Russel Wallace: Letters and Reminiscences.* New York, 1916.

R. K. MURTON

"Endocrine Stress"   "The Significance of Endocrine Stress in Population Control," in *Ibis*, CIX (1967), 622–23.

THE ROYAL SOCIETY

   E. B. P[oulton]. "Alfred Russel Wallace, 1823–1913," in *Proceedings of the Royal Society of London*, XCV-B (1923–24).

Sources and Notes

ALFRED RUSSEL WALLACE

"Monkeys of the Amazon"

"On the Monkeys of the Amazon" in *Proceedings of the Zoological Society of London*, XX (1852), 107–10.

Travels on the Amazon

A Narrative of Travels on the Amazon and Rio Negro, with an Account of the Native Tribes, and Observations on the Climate, Geology, and Natural History of the Amazon Valley. London, 1853; rev. edn., London, New York and Melbourne, 1889. The 1889 edition is used throughout.

"Introduction of New Species"

"On the Law which has Regulated the Introduction of New Species," in *Annals and Magazine of Natural History*, ser. 2, XVI (Sept. 1855), 184–96.

"Tendency to Depart from the Original Type"

"On the Tendency of Varieties to Depart Indefinitely from the Original Type," in *Proceedings of the Linnean Society (Zoology)*, III (1858), 53–57. (Wallace's part of the "joint papers.")

Malay Archipelago

The Malay Archipelago: the Land of the Orang-utan and the Bird of Paradise; a Narrative of Travel with Studies of Man and Nature. London, 1869; 10th edn. (rev.), 1890. Revised edition reprinted, New York, Dover Publications, Inc., 1962. The 1962 edition is used throughout.

Darwinism

Darwinism: An Exposition of the Theory of Natural Selection, with Some of Its Applications. New York, 1889.

My Life

My Life: a Record of Events and Opinions. New York, 1905. (2 vols.)

NOTES

1	The Royal Society, i		*the Amazons*, 288–301
3	Wallace, *My Life*,	69	*Ibid.*, 208
	I:256	70	*Ibid.*, 217
13–14	*Ibid.*, 109–10	70	Wallace, *Travels on*
14	*Ibid.*, 191		*the Amazon*, 290–91
16	*Ibid.*, 236–37	71–76	Bates, *Naturalist on*
23	Bates, *Naturalist on*		*the Amazons*, 208–19
	the Amazons, 1	76–79	Wallace, *Travels on*
25	Wallace, *My Life*,		*the Amazon*, 120–22
	I:287	80	*Ibid.*, 115–16
30–33	Wallace, *Travels on*	80–82	Wallace, *My Life*,
	the Amazon, 300–307		I:315–16
34–35	Wallace, *Ibid.*, 16–18	82–84	Bates, *Naturalist on*
35	Bates, *Naturalist on*		*the Amazons*, 333–36
	the Amazons, 40–43	85	Wallace, *Travels on*
36	Wallace, *Travels on*		*the Amazon*, 4
	the Amazon, 12, 148–	87–91	*Ibid.*, 170–74
	49	91–92	*Ibid.*, 166
36–37	*Ibid.*, 24–25	92–93	Wallace, *My Life*,
37–38	*Ibid.*, 29		I:288–89
38–40	Bates, *Naturalist on*	93–97	Wallace, *Travels on*
	the Amazons, 27–29		*the Amazon*, 189–94
40–44	*Ibid.*, 32–35	97–100	Bates, *Naturalist on*
45	*Ibid.*, 92		*the Amazons*, 301–30
47–49	*Ibid.*, 43–45	101–03	*Ibid.*, 358–63
49–53	*Ibid.*, 66–86	104	Wallace, *My Life*,
53–55	*Ibid.*, 131–32		I:288
55–61	Wallace, *Travels on*	107–10	Bates, *Naturalist on*
	the Amazon, 92–112		*the Amazons*, 62–65
61–62	Wallace, *My Life*,	111–13	*Ibid.* (1863 edn.),
	I:317–18		I:297–300
62	*Ibid.*, 320	113–16	*Ibid.* (1962 edn.),
62	Wallace, *Travels on*		113–15
	the Amazon, 246–47	116–17	*Ibid.*, 406–407
62–63	Wallace, *My Life*,	118–20	Wallace, *Travels on*
	I:316–20, *passim*		*the Amazon*, 114, 281–
63–68	Bates, *Naturalist on*		84

120–21   *Ibid.*, 324–25
121–22   *Ibid.*, 326–27
122–23   Wallace, "On the Monkeys of the Amazon," 110
123   Wallace, *Travels on the Amazon*, 328
124   Bates, *Naturalist on the Amazons*, 459
125–26   Wallace, *Travels on the Amazon*, 210–12
126–31   *Ibid.*, 250–79
131–32   Wallace, letter to Richard Spruce, a friend still in South America, *My Life*, I:309–10
132–33   Wallace, *My Life*, I:314–15
133   *Ibid.*, 327
135–38   Bates, *Naturalist on the Amazons*, 447–56
138–39   *Ibid.*, 458–59
139   *Ibid.* (1863 edn.), Preface
141   Wallace, *My Life*, I:336
143   Wallace, *Malay Archipelago*, 2
148–50   *Ibid.*, 16–19
150–51   *Ibid.*, 75–76
151–53   *Ibid.*, 115–17
153–54   *Ibid.*, 155–56
154   *Ibid.*, 7–8
155–57   *Ibid.*, 191–93
157–59   *Ibid.*, 234–36
160   *Ibid.*, 317

161   Huxley, *Man's Place in Nature*, 36
163–67   Wallace, *Malay Archipelago*, 30–47 *passim*
167–70   *Ibid.*, 32–36
170–71   *Ibid.*, 282–83
171–74   *Ibid.*, 56–58
174–77   *Ibid.*, 97–102
177–180   *Ibid.*, 305–307
181   *Ibid.*, 377
183   Marchant, *Alfred Russel Wallace*, 194
184–86   *Ibid.*, 419–439 *passim*
186–92   *Ibid.*, 309–340 *passim*
192–95   *Ibid.*, 380–391
195–96   *Ibid.*, 251–53
196–97   *Ibid.*, 431–32
197–98   *Ibid.*, 423–24
198–99   Wallace, *My Life*, I:384
200   Marchant, *Alfred Russel Wallace*, 474
201   Wallace, *Darwinism*, iv
203   Murton, "Endocrine Stress," 623
206   Wallace, "Introduction of New Species," 186
207   Wallace, *Malay Archipelago*, 13
209   Wallace, "Tendency to Depart from the Original Type," p. 57
213–17   Bates, "Lepidoptera: Heliconidae," 502–15

Index

*Variations in names are in parentheses; scientific names are in-
cluded when used in the text.*

Index

Celebes, 133, 144, 155, 220, 224

Ceram, 179

Cerambycidae, 149

Chambers, Robert (1802–1871), 6–7, 19–20, 105–106, 206

Cicinnurus regius, see Paradisaea regia

cipó (sipo), 39, 83, 84

clearwing, 109

climate and weather, 28, 30, 41, 42–44, 50, 65–66, 69–70, 73–76, 86–87, 89–90, 100; dry season, 43, 55, 69, 74–75, 101, 108; wet season, 43, 55, 64–65, 75–76

Coari (Coary), Braz., 77, 119

cockroaches, 197–98

Coleoptera, 7, 15–16, 29, 40, 75, 109–110, 149–50, 221

collecting, 7–10, 15–16, 21, 28, 41–42, 44, 91, 97–99, 130–31, 132, 134, 137, 139, 148–50, 161, 183, 189, 194–95, 205

Collegiate School (Leicester), 15

Columbina, 74

conservation, 30, 134, 138–39

continental drift, 147, 207, 221, 225

continental shelf, 146, 181–82, 221

convergent evolution, 105, 115–16, 212, 221

Copsychus saularis (Copsychus amoenus), 153

cotingas, 71, 78, 79, 80–82, 84; *see also* entries under names of species

crab-eating macaque (hare-lip monkey), 168–69

"creation," *see* species, origin of

crested bobwhite (white-crested Brazilian pheasant), 127

crimson-breasted barbet (rosy barbet), 153

crocodile, 165–66

curassow, 100

curupira, 35

Dampier, William (1652–1715), 185

Darwin, Charles Robert (1809–1882), 3–4, 6–8, 19, 20, 135, 147, 183, 199, 200, 201, 207, 210–11, 214, 225

Darwinism (Wallace), 200, 201

Desmoncus, 39–40

Dinopium javanense (Chrysonotus tiga), 153

dipterous insects, 76, 222

Dobo (Dobbo), Aroe Is., 187, 188, 189

durian, 162, 165, 170–74

Dyaks (tribe), 164, 165–66, 167, 172

Earth, age of, 4, 5, 18, 204

earthquakes, 147, 155–57, 158

education, 6–7, 12, 15

Edwards, William Henry (1822–1909), 21

entomology, 15, 222; *see also* insects

epiphytes, 29, 84

Index

Ploceus hypoxanthus, 152, 153
polymorphism, 217, 223; *see also* mimetic polymorphism
pompadour cotinga, 79
population, principle of, 17–18, 207–208, 223
porpoises, 59
Potos flavus (*Cercoleptes*), 40
predator, 211–12, 215, 217–18, 223
Principles of Geology (Lyell), 18–19
protective coloration, 81, 105, 111–13, 177–80, 212, 223–24
purple-breasted cotinga, 84
python, 166

Rain forest, *see* tropical rain forest
rainfall, 30, 221, 224
Ramphastos tucanus (*R. cuvieri*), 99
Ramphastos vitellinus, 42
red-capped cardinal (red-headed tanager), 51
Rio Negro, 46, 61–63, 85, 106–107, 118, 119–21, 123, 132, 220; color of, 61–62, 106, 119–20
rivers, 45–68, 106–107, 118–23; animals of, 106–107, 120–21, 122–23; colors of, 58, 60, 61–62, 72, 97, 106, 118–20; *see also* entries under names of rivers, water barriers

roads and paths, 41, 45, 86, 87–89, 138–39
Ross, Sir James Clark (1800–1862), 9
Royal Botanic Gardens, Kew, Eng., 9
Royal Geographical Society, 135
Royal Society, The, 2, 227
rubber, 32

St. Ann's flower, 79
Salinas (now Salinópolis), Braz., 23
San Carlos, Venez., 85
sandfly, 73, 91
Santarém, Braz., 46, 47, 55, 69, 71, 72–73, 77, 133, 219
São Lúiz de Maranhão (Maranham), Braz., 41, 138
São Paulo de Olivença, Braz., 134, 135–36, 137, 219
Sapurara (Tabatinga), Braz., 137
Sarawak, Borneo, 133, 144, 220
science, 203–204, 218; and religion, 4, 5, 6, 7, 203–204; in nineteenth century England, 2, 3–4, 6–10, 135, 183, 199–200
sea, depth of, 146, 154, 181–82; *see also* Wallace's Line
seasons, *see* climate and weather
Semioptera wallacei, 181–82, 195–97
Simanggang (Simunjon) River, 163

Index

White bellbird, 81
white cockatoo, 154
white-throated toucan (Cu-
    vier's toucan), 99

Yellow fever, 47

Zoology, 224

X98163

Beddall, Barbara G
  Wallace and Bates in the Tropics; an introduction to the theory of natural selection, based on the writings of Alfred Russel Wallace and Henry Walter Bates, edited by Barbara G. Beddall. ₁New York₁ Macmillan ₁1969₁

  ix, 241 p. 2 maps, 2 ports. 21 cm.

  Includes bibliographical references.

  1. Natural selection. 2. Wallace, Alfred Russel, 1823–1913. 3. Bates, Henry Walter, 1825–1892.   I. Title.

QH366.B417   575.01′62   69–12174
                                                              MARC

  Library of Congress   ₁30-2₁